THREAD THE NEEDLE

D0992758

COORDINATING AUTHOR
JACK BOOTH

DAVID BOOTH
JO PHENIX LARRY SWARTZ

ORCHARD SCHOOL

IMPRESSIONS

HOLT, RINEHART AND WINSTON OF CANADA, LIMITED

Executive Editor: Jocelyn Klemm
Project Editor: Diane Taylor
Developmental Editor: Grant Heckman
Editorial Assistant: Christine McGarity
Permissions Editor: Pamela O'Brien
Production Editor: Elizabeth Reid
Art Director: Mary Opper
Designer: Martin Gould
Layout Artists: Gary Beelik, Julia Naimska, Sandra Quigley
Cover Illustrator: Doug Martin

Copyright © 1987, Holt, Rinehart and Winston of Canada, Limited. All rights reserved.

Canadian Cataloguing in Publication Data

Main entry under title:

Thread the needle

(Impressions)
for use in schools.
ISBN 0-03-921903-8

1. Readers (Elementary). I. Booth, Jack, 1946-
II. Series: Impressions (Toronto, Ont.)

PE1119.T48 1987 428.6 C87-093396-5

Illustrations
Nick Vitacco: pp. 6-7; *Sarah Battersby:* pp. 8-9, 112-113; *Barbara Klunder:* pp. 10-16; *Maurice Vellecoup:* pp. 19-23, 170-171; *Kellie Jobson:* pp. 26-31, 286-287; *Frank Hammond:* pp. 32-35; *Robert McCloskey:* pp. 37-49; *Martin Gould:* pp. 50-51, 179; *Bob Fortier:* pp. 52-55; *Allen Shugar:* pp. 56-63; *Laurie LaFrance:* pp. 64-65, 220-221, 268-273; *Joe Morse:* pp. 66-67; *Louise Fitzhugh:* pp. 68-77; *Vince Mancuso:* pp. 78-79; *Doug Martin:* pp. 80-83, 114-115; *Michael Reinhart:* pp. 84-89, 116-117, 132-137, 199-202; *Malcolm Cullen:* pp. 90-95; *Wojtek Gorczynski:* pp. 96-99; *Paul McCusker:* pp. 100-109, 230-235, 274-285; *Brian McPhee:* pp. 110-111; *Alanna Marohnic:* pp. 119-125, 206-210; *Donna Gordon:* pp. 127-131; *Laura Fernandez:* pp. 143-148; *Maureen Paxton:* pp. 154-157; *Henry van der Linde:* pp. 159-163, 184-187; *Shel Silverstein:* pp. 164-167; *Allan and Deborah Drew-Brook-Cormack:* pp. 168-169, 204-205; *Chris Middleton:* pp. 172-176; *Sarah Jane English:* pp. 184-193; *Joanne Fitzgerald:* pp. 211-219; *Avril Orloff:* pp. 222-223; *Tracy Burk:* pp. 224-225; *Provincial Archives of British Columbia:* p. 226, HP41551; pp. 228-229, HP 79083; *Emily Carr:* p. 227, "Indian Church," 1929, oil on canvas, 108.6 × 68.9 cm, courtesy of the Art Gallery of Ontario, Toronto: Bequest of Charles S. Band, 1970; p. 228, "House Front, Gold Harbour," oil on board, 61.7 × 91.5 cm, courtesy of the Art Gallery of Vancouver; *Irene Brady:* pp. 236-241; *Clive Dobson:* pp. 150-153, 242-243, 245-247, 259; *Ken Stampnick:* pp. 249-254; Ron Watts: pp. 260-261; *Tony Thomas:* pp. 262-266, 267 (top); *RCMP:* p. 267 (bottom).

The authors and publishers gratefully acknowledge the educators listed below for their contribution to the development of this program:
Ron Benson *Coordinator of Primary Education Scarborough Board of Education*
Ethel Buchanan *Language Arts Consultant Winnipeg, Manitoba*
Margaret Crocker *Teacher and Vice Principal Bedford District School Board, Halifax County*
William Fagan *Language Arts Coordinator Roman Catholic School Board for St. John's, Newfoundland*
Ruth Fulton *Supervisor of Elementary Education District No. 20, Saint John, New Brunswick*
June Gravel *Language Arts Coordinator Dufferin-Peel Roman Catholic Separate School Board*
Pat Hogan *Language Arts Consultant Calgary Board of Education Coordinator Calgary Writing Project*
Margaret Joyce *Language Arts Consultant School Unit No. 3, Charlottetown, P.E.I.*
Linda Kaser *Coordinator, Language Arts and English K-12 Richmond School District*
Roberta McKay *Consultant, Language Arts Social Studies Edmonton Public Schools*
Ina Mary Rutherford *Supervisor of Reading and Primary Education Bruce County Board of Education*
Janice Petracek *Executive Assistant to the Deputy Director of Education Regina School Division*

Printed in Canada 5 91 90

Table of Contents

Where It's At

We all love to laugh, and we laugh at the strangest things! Talking horses, people in trouble, real-life situations, imaginary events—almost anything can be the basis for humour. Sometimes we have to relax and not worry too much about how accurate the descriptions are; the whole idea may be to turn sense into nonsense, to see life in a fun-house mirror.

The Strongman thought he'd try Jack again. He got him a hogshead barrel and rigged up a big bail on it like a bucket. Brought that to Jack, says, "Jack, the King wants a little water fetched in this bucket. I'm fryin' us a calf for dinner or I'd go. Here's the bucket." And he set it down, went on back in the house.

Jack couldn't even lift the bucket off the ground. He went to the door, hollered, "Where's the shovel?"

"What do you want with the shovel, Jack?"

"Why I wouldn't fool with takin' water anywhere in a little bitty old bucket like that. Hand me the shovel here. I'll just dig the well up and move it nearer the kitchen where they can get at it a lot handier."

"Just let it go, Jack. I'll fetch the water up directly. Now you leave the shovel where it's at."

(from *Jack and Old Strongman*, compiled by Richard Chase)

Tall tales are fun to read and even more fun to tell.

In this section, you will meet all types of humorous selections, from far-fetched yarns to rhymes from your own schoolyard. Join in the print laughter—this is "where it's at."

Swinging on a Star

words by J. Burke, music by Van Heusen

Would you like to swing on a star,
Carry moonbeams home in a jar,
And be better off than you are,
Or would you rather be a mule?

A mule is an animal with long funny ears,
He kicks up at anything he hears,
His back is brawny
And his brain is weak,
He's just plain stupid
With a stubborn streak,
And by the way if you hate to go to school,
You may grow up to be a mule.

Or would you like to swing on a star,
Carry moonbeams home in a jar,
And be better off than you are,
Or would you rather be a pig?

A pig is an animal with dirt on his face,
His shoes are a terrible disgrace,
He's got no manners
When he eats his food,
He's fat and lazy
And extremely rude,
But if you don't care a feather or a fig,
You may grow up to be a pig.

Or would you like to swing on a star,
Carry moonbeams home in a jar,
And be better off than you are,
Or would you rather be a fish?

A fish won't do anything but swim in a brook,
He can't write his name or read a book,
To fool the people
Is his only thought,
And though he's slippery,
He still gets caught,
But then if that sort of life is what you wish,
You may grow up to be a fish.

And all the monkeys aren't in the zoo,
Ev'ry day you meet quite a few,
So you see it's all up to you.
You can be better than you are,

You could be swinging on a star.

© Copyright 1944 by Burke/Van Heusen Inc., A Division of Bourne Company, New York—Used by Permission of Bourne Music Canada Limited, Toronto, Canada (Canadian Agents).

from

The Boy Who Turned into a TV Set

by Stephen Manes

Ogden Pettibone watched television all the time. He watched game shows and news shows, police shows and educational shows, comedies and dramas, public service announcements, weather reports, cartoons, and commercials. Ogden would watch anything. Except soap operas. Ogden thought soap operas were dumb.

"If you keep watching TV so much," his mother often told him, "you might just turn into a television." Ogden always laughed when she said that. He knew she was only kidding. He knew people didn't really turn into TV sets.

One horrible day after school, Ogden came home to find that the Pettibones' television was broken.

"Broken!" he screamed. "How could it be broken?"

"It doesn't get a picture, and the only sound it makes is a sizzling noise, and smoke comes from the back when you turn it on," said his mother. "Someone will come out and fix it tomorrow."

"Tomorrow!" Ogden wailed. "But I need to watch my programs today!"

"Read a book for a change," Mrs. Pettibone suggested.

"Phooey," said Ogden, but he took his mother's advice. He went to the bookshelf and looked for a volume called *How to Repair Your Own TV*. Skimming through it, he found the information he was looking for. "No picture; sizzling, smoke: BIG TROUBLE. Do not attempt to fix this yourself, or you will be sorry. Unplug the set and call a repairman."

Ogden frowned, put the book back on the shelf, had some milk and cake, and watched his goldfish swim around the aquarium. It was slightly more interesting than staring at the blank TV screen.

"Dinnertime!" his father finally shouted from the kitchen.

Ogden opened his mouth to say he'd be right there, but instead a deep voice came out. "We'll be right back after this important message," it said. Ogden was very surprised.

"Don't be funny, Ogden," his dad scolded.

"I've never seen clothes so white!" Ogden exclaimed in a woman's voice that startled him even more. "How do you do it?"

His mother frowned. "Og, what's wrong with you? Come to dinner while it's hot."

Ogden sat down at the table. "I use Ultra Wash," he said in another woman's voice. "It has twenty-seven percent more cleaning power." This wasn't what Ogden wanted to say at all. It was just what came out of his mouth when he opened it and tried to speak. He couldn't understand it.

"Enough, Ogden," said his father. "I don't think you're amusing."

Neither did Ogden. He felt as though he were a dummy on the lap of some invisible ventriloquist. "Ultra Wash gets your clothes so bright, your friends will not believe the sight!" a chorus sang cheerfully through his lips. Embarrassed, Ogden slumped down in his chair.

"Sit up straight and stop this foolishness," his mother commanded. "If you can't behave, you'll go up to your room without supper. Now, tell us what you did in school today."

Ogden thought he must be going crazy. He tried to tell them about the guinea pig that had triplets, but what came out of his mouth was someone else's voice saying, "Well, that just about wraps up our show."

"It certainly does!" snapped his mother. "Go up to your room, and don't come back till you're ready to behave."

Ogden wanted to protest. But when he opened his mouth, a voice said, "See you same time tomorrow."

"Get going! Right now!" his father shouted.

Ogden left the table. He plodded up the stairs and flopped down on his bed. "I can't understand it!" he said to himself, making very sure he didn't open his mouth. "What's happening to me?"

He let out a big sigh. Before he had a chance to finish it, a new voice squealed with glee. "Whee!" it exclaimed. "I've been chocolatized!"

Ogden clapped his hand over his mouth to keep anything else from coming out. Whatever was going on, it was worse than a bad case of hiccups.

In fact, it was a lot like hiccups. Ogden tried holding his breath. But after a while he began turning blue and had to come up for air. "Good evening," a robust voice said as Ogden gasped. "President Ablefinger announced today that he believes more money should be spent on peanut butter research."

Ogden slammed his jaws shut. Maybe some water would help. He went to the bathroom and filled a cup. But as he opened his mouth to take a sip, he heard an elderly voice say, "False teeth a problem?" The water drowned the next words out, but when the glass was empty, the voice declared, "I can eat anything now!" and took a loud chomp on an invisible apple.

Hiccup cures didn't always work on Ogden's hiccups, and it was obvious they weren't going to work on this problem, either. He went into his bedroom, turned out the lights, lay down on his bed, closed his eyes, and tried to think.

It wasn't much use. He didn't have any idea what was the matter with him. And how could he explain his predicament to his parents if every time he opened his mouth, something stupid came out? He sighed again. "A swarm of giant fruit flies attacked the town of Quagmire, Montana, today," said his lips in a resonant baritone.

Ogden shut his mouth and opened his eyes. Suddenly he noticed that his T-shirt seemed to be glowing. He untucked it to take a closer look.

The T-shirt wasn't glowing at all. His stomach was. Right above his bellybutton was the six o'clock news in living colour. A rocket on his tummy-screen blasted off toward his chest.

Ogden's jaw dropped in amazement, and he bellowed a deafening rocketlike roar. "Wow!" he thought. "I've turned into a TV!"

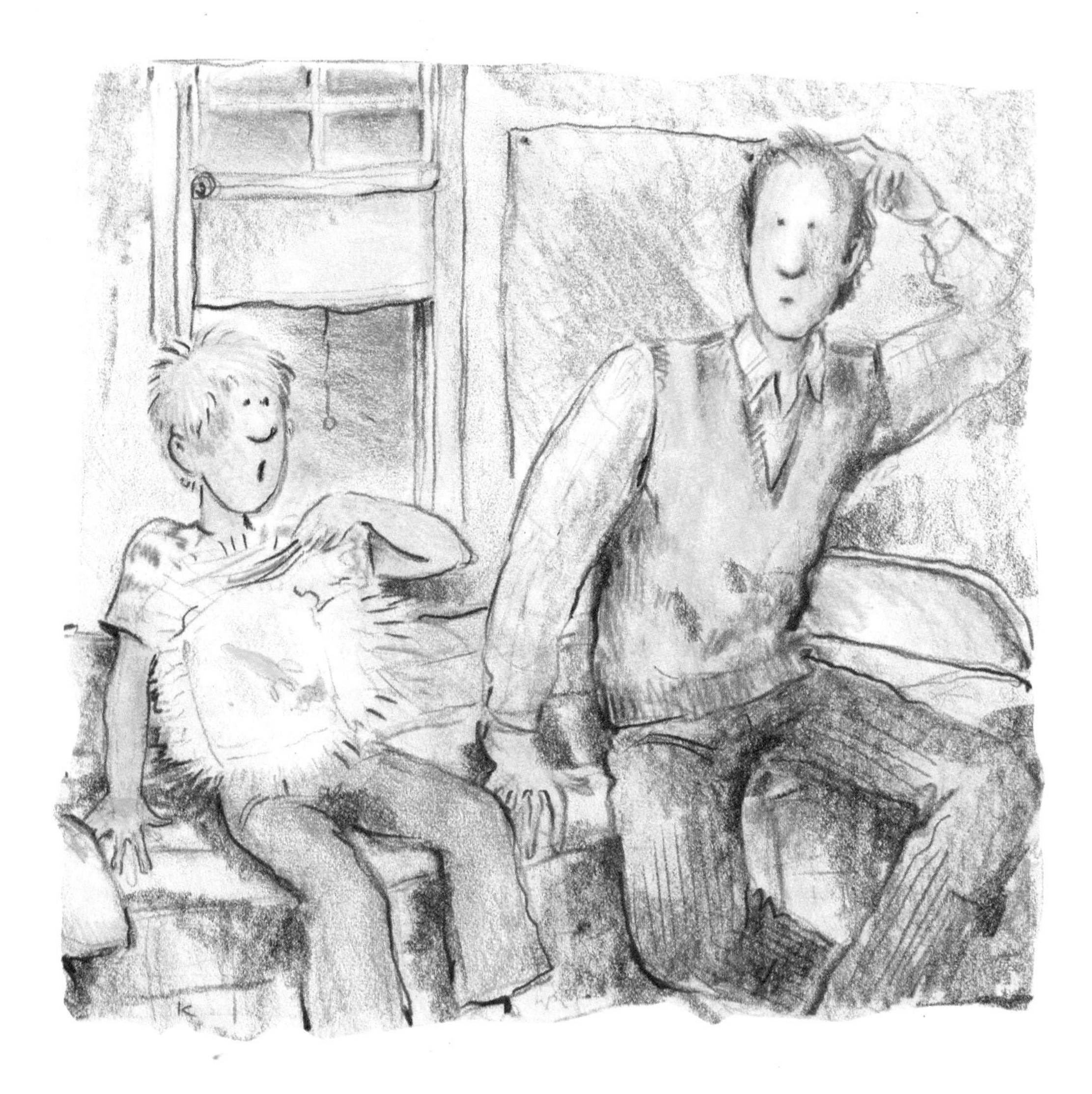

Ogden's parents heard the blastoff.

"What's all that racket? Are you okay?" his father hollered, rushing up the stairs.

Ogden kept his mouth shut.

"Did you fall out of bed or something? What was all that noise?"

Ogden pointed to his belly. The rocket disappeared into the clouds.

"It's the six o'clock news!" his father cried. "But where's the sound?"

Ogden pointed to his mouth and opened wide. "Tomorrow, the astronauts will attempt the first game of baseball ever played in outer space," he said in the voice of the reporter who appeared on the screen. Then he closed his mouth again.

"Open up a minute," his father said. "I want to hear whether they caught those sneak thieves."

Ogden obediently loosened his jaws. The criminals were still at large, but the police had recovered the stolen truckload of tennis shoes.

"What's going on here?" Mrs. Pettibone wanted to know.

"Ogden's turned into a TV set," his father explained.

"I always said he would," his mother gloated.

"How did it happen?" his father asked him.

Ogden shrugged. He knew as little about it as they did.

"Well, enough's enough," said his mother. "Shut yourself off and come back down to dinner."

Ogden shook his head.

"Why not?" His father scowled.

Ogden grabbed a pad and pencil from his desk and scribbled the words, "I can't."

"Don't be ridiculous," his father said.

Ogden scribbled furiously. "I'm telling the truth," he wrote. "I don't know how this happened. I can't shut myself off. And I can't talk, because every time I open my mouth, TV sounds come out."

"Hmmmm," his father hummed thoughtfully.

"What shall we do?" his mother worried.

"I think we'd better have the doctor take a look at Ogden in the morning."

"And in the meantime?" Ogden wrote.

"Well, as long as our TV's broken, you might as well make yourself useful," his father replied. "Come downstairs and let us watch you."

Ogden ate supper. He felt rather uncomfortable making TV sounds between each bite, but his parents were very understanding.

Then they all went into the living room. Ogden sat in front of the broken television and took off his T-shirt. While his parents stared at him from the couch, he watched his amazing belly in a mirror at their feet. The mirror made the picture look backward, but he preferred that to the topsy-turvy view and stiff neck he got when he looked straight down at his screen.

"Excellent reception," said his father during a commercial break, "even though the picture is a bit small. And this remote control is the best yet. If we want the sound louder, all we have to do is ask. Maybe we won't have to have our old set fixed after all."

"But Ogden only gets one channel," Mrs. Pettibone reminded her husband.

"Forgot about that," said Mr. Pettibone.

Ogden hoped they weren't serious. Much as he enjoyed being the centre of attention, he still felt funny about his glowing stomach and contrary vocal cords. He hoped the doctor would be able to figure out what was wrong with him.

"Open up, dear," Mrs. Pettibone requested. "The commercial's over."

Ogden sighed into action.

from

Me and the Weirdos

by Jane Sutton

If your mother gargles with orange juice and changes her name to Squirrel, if your father plants weeds in the back yard, and if your sister collects empty can labels for a hobby, then, like ten-year-old Cindy Krinkle, you may feel you are living with weirdos. Roger Snooterman, the paperboy, says Cindy ought to be embarrassed, and she starts to wonder. She decides to help her family "unweird" themselves—whether they like it or not.

I decided that having a weird family was causing me much too much trouble. Roger Snooterman was right. They were just plain embarrassing.

I made up my mind to think of a plan to get them to stop being weird. Talking to them hadn't worked. And my silence plan hadn't lasted through one pancakes-with-strawberries breakfast.

I decided to try something new. I thought that if my family tried acting normal, they might like it and decide to make it a habit.

The next Saturday, my father was busy planting dandelions and crabgrass in the front yard. My mother was trimming the rocket ship and penguin hedges. Sarah was twirling her baton while she roller-skated in the driveway. It was an unusually warm day for May.

I sat on the front steps trying to think of a normal activity for my family to do. I figured that being with other people might help. Maybe they stayed weird because they hung around together too much without seeing normal people.

I saw a family go by in a station wagon. The kids in the back had pails, shovels, rubber rafts, and flippers.

The beach! I thought. I couldn't remember ever going to the beach with my family. I went to Patti's parents' swimming pool club lots of times. Everybody acted normal there . . .

I figured that the beach would be a perfect place to unweird my family—they would be surrounded by normal people. They couldn't help learning to act normal!

I ran into the front yard. "Let's go to the beach," I said.

My father got into one of his big-word moods: "You, Cindy, are a true inspiration," he said. "There is nothing quite so lovely as the beach—the magic place where land meets water. And incidentally, my increasing perspiration as I labour with these plants makes the idea additionally appealing."

"I haven't been to the beach in years," said my mother. She threw down her pruning shears. "Let's go," she said.

My mother told Sarah that we were going to the beach. We all changed into our beach clothes. Then we piled into our van, which has a big painting of a rainbow on the outside.

We were about to leave when my mother said, "Wait a minute!" She jumped out of the van and ran around it three times. While she ran, she flapped her elbows like a bird and made crowing noises. Luckily, we were in our own driveway. I don't think anyone saw her.

When she got back in the van, she said, "Now we should have good weather at the beach. That was a sun dance one of my fencing students taught me."

On the way to the beach, we saw a teenage girl hitchhiking.

My father pulled over to pick her up. She climbed into the van, saying, "Thanks a lot!" Then she looked around and got very quiet. She looked kind of scared.

I didn't blame her for being scared. I saw her look at my father. He had his safari hat on to keep the sun off the bald top of his head. His arms were covered with tattoos he had painted with water-colours. The tattoos on his left arm were pictures of animals. Along his right arm, he had painted, "Have you hugged an airplane cleaner today?"

I saw the hitchhiker look at my mother. My mother doesn't have

HONK IF YOU LOVE TONY BENNETT?
have you hugged an
plant cleaner today?

a bathing suit. So she was wearing a pink ballerina tutu and, of course, her red sneakers. Her grey frizzy hair was sticking out more than ever.

The hitchhiker took a quick glance behind her at Sarah. She was wearing a straw hat over her bright red hair and a white karate suit to keep the sun off her fair skin.

I had a normal bathing suit on. But I guess one normal person can't cancel out three weirdos. The hitchhiker stared straight ahead, out the windshield. Her lips were moving a little. Maybe she was praying.

My father gave the hitchhiker a lecture. He told her she shouldn't hitchhike. "You never know what kind of strange people will pick you up," he said.

"I know what you mean," said the hitchhiker.

When we got to the beach, the hitchhiker started to rush out of the van. "Wait just a minute," my father said.

The hitchhiker kept her hand on the door handle and listened.

"I don't want you hitchhiking anymore," said my father.

"Oh, I won't," the hitchhiker said. "I promise."

"Here's money to rent a bicycle to ride home," my father said. "There's a bike rental shop near the snack bar."

The hitchhiker stared at him. Then she stuffed the money into her pocket and said, "Thanks." She got out of the van and ran toward the beach.

My family just may have cured her of hitchhiking.

"Rats!" said my father. "I should have told her to look for a bicycle with an umbrella on it."

We got a good spot on the beach, right near the water. I was hoping my family would look around and get an idea of what you're supposed to do at the beach. People were wading, sunbathing, listening to radios, playing cards, throwing Frisbees . . .

"Who wants to play catch?" I asked my family. "I brought along a beach ball. We can throw it around and maybe some other people will play with us."

"Maybe later," said my father. "I want to fly my kite now."

He started flying this weird kite he had made. It looks like a hamburger. In fact, he calls it The Flying Hamburger.

My mother didn't want to play catch either. She was busy practising cartwheels in the sand.

Sarah just wanted to read the dictionary she had brought. She sat in the sun with her karate suit on. I know she has to protect her skin from the sun, but did she have to wear mittens and take them off each time she turned the page?

I could feel people on the beach staring at us. I would have liked to bury my head in the sand. But I lay on the blanket and pretended to be enjoying the sun.

After a while, I heard a commotion. I looked up and saw my father struggling with The Flying Hamburger. It had fallen on a Frisbee player and the Frisbee player was tangled up in the string. When the Frisbee player got untangled, he and the three other players moved to another part of the beach.

My father put away The Flying Hamburger.

"How about going wading?" I suggested. The water was too cold for swimming.

"Yes, let's try out the Queen Miranda," said my mother.

My father said, "Aye aye, Captain."

I hadn't realized that my mother had brought along her toy boat. It was bad enough that she played with the Queen Miranda at home in the bathtub. But now she was going to play with it on a public beach where everyone could see her! I decided I didn't want to go in the water with my parents after all.

My mother and father put the boat in the water. They giggled as it got tossed around the waves. They made lots of noise being enthusiastic. "There it goes!" they shouted. "Oops, it almost sank! Whee!"

I tried to read a book. But I couldn't concentrate on it. I kept reading the same paragraph.

After a while, I gave up reading and looked around. I counted fourteen people sitting near us. Fourteen, plus four Frisbee players,

Queen

plus one hitchhiker—that made nineteen more people who now knew that my family was weird. This beach outing was not working out as I had wanted it to.

I looked at the family next to us. There was a grandmother playing with a baby. The mother and father were sitting in beach chairs and reading newspapers. They all wore normal bathing suits. Why couldn't my family be normal, like them?

The people on the other side of us were cooking hot dogs and hamburgers. They had the right idea—they were going to eat hamburgers, not fly one! There was a mother and a father and a boy and a girl. I wished my family were as normal as that family. They even had a normal-looking dog. They probably didn't have any dumb sea urchin at home.

I asked Sarah if she wanted to help me dig a big hole and bury each other in it. It seemed like a pretty normal thing to do at the beach.

She wouldn't even look up from her dictionary. "Don't bother me," she said. "I want to finish the B's today."

My parents were still playing with the Queen Miranda. At least my father's watercolour tattoos had washed off in the water. But he still had that safari hat on with his long, scraggly hair hanging down from it. And my mother had that ballerina outfit.

"Hey, Cindy, come play with the boat!" my mother, the beach ballerina, shouted.

Quickly, I lay down and pretended to be asleep. No one could tell she was talking to me if I didn't answer.

I guess my parents got tired of the boat after a while. I heard my father say, "I think I will embark on a walk. A walk on the beach is enormously exhilarating."

My mother lay down on the beach blanket next to me. "My sun dance must have worked," she said. "The weather is beautiful—you already have some new freckles on your nose, Cindy."

I didn't say anything. She seemed to fall asleep and I fell asleep too. I had a dream that Roger Snooterman was on the beach laughing and pointing at me.

When I woke up, my mother was packing up the Queen Miranda and The Flying Hamburger. "It must be getting late," she said. "I'm starved." My mother never wears a watch. She goes on stomach time.

"Where's Daddy?" I asked.

"He hasn't gotten back from his walk yet," my mother said.

Sarah started calling, "Daddy-O! Daddy-cakes!"

"Can't you just call him Daddy?" I asked. My face felt red. And it wasn't just from sunburn.

"Don't be silly," Sarah said. "If I yelled 'Daddy,' every father on the beach would turn around."

As far as I could tell, every father on the beach *was* turning to look at her. And so was every mother, sister, brother, aunt, and uncle.

Then we heard a loud voice. It was the lifeguard talking over his bullhorn. "Attention, please!" he said. "I have a lost man here. He's about forty-five years old . . . "

We looked at the lifeguard, and there was my father standing on the big chair behind him.

"He's wearing a safari hat . . . " the lifeguard said.

"Smith!" my mother shouted.

"And he answers to the name of Smith Krinkle," the lifeguard said.

My mother ran toward the lifeguard chair. When my father saw her, he waved and climbed down. He and my mother hugged. He picked her up and whirled her around because he was glad to see her.

Everybody on the beach laughed and cheered.

"I couldn't remember where our blanket was," my father explained.

I thought, *I am mortified.* I wasn't sure if *mortified* was the right word for the way I felt. While Sarah jumped up and down and cheered, I looked it up in her dictionary. It said: "*Mortify*—To hurt someone's pride or self-respect." I was mortified all right.

We got ready to leave. I was grateful for one thing—we hadn't run into anyone we knew.

from

Dear Mr. Henshaw

by Beverly Cleary

May 12,

Dear Mr. Henshaw,

My teacher read your book about the dog to Our class. It was funny. We licked it.

Your freind,
Leigh Botts
(boy)

December 3

Dear Mr. Henshaw,

I am the boy who wrote to you last year when I was in the second grade. Maybe you didn't get my LeTter. This year I read the book I wrote to you about called Ways to Amuse a Dog. It is the first thick book with chapters that I have read.

The boy's father said city dogs were bored so Joe could not Keep the dog unless he could think up seven ways to amuse it. I have a black dog. His name is Bandit. He is a nice dog.

If you answer I get to put your letter on the bulletin board. My teacher taught me a trick about friend. The i goes before e so that at the end it will spell end.

Keep in tutch.

Your friend,
Leigh (Lēē) Botts

Dear Mr. Henshaw, November 13

I am in the fourth grade now. I made a diorama of "Ways to Amuse a Dog," the book I wrote to you about two times before. Now our teacher is making us write to authors for Book week. I got your answer to my letter last year, but it was only printed. Please would you write to me in your own handwriting? I am a great enjoyer of your books.

My favourite character in the book was Joe's Dad because he didn't get mad when Joe amused his dog by playing a tape of a lady singing, and his dog sat and howled like he was singing too, Bandit does the same thing when he hears singing.

Your best reader

Leigh Botts

OOWWVV

← Bandit singing

December 2

Dear Mr. Henshaw,

I got to thinking about "Ways to Amuse a Dog." When Joe took his dog to the park and taught him to slide down the slide, wouldn't some grownups come along and say he couldn't let his dog use the slide? Around here grownups, who are mostly real old with cats, get mad if dogs aren't on leashes every minute. I hate living in a mobile home park.

I saw your picture on the back of the book. When I grow up I want to be a famous book writer with a beard like you.

I am sending you my picture. It is last year's picture. My hair is longer now. With all the millions of kids, how would you know who I am if I don't send you my picture?

Your favourite reader,

Leigh Botts

Enclosure: picture of me.

(We are studying business letters.)

Dear Mr. Henshaw, October 2

I am in the fifth grade now. You might like to know that I gave a book report on "Ways to Amuse a Dog." The class liked it. I got an A-. The minus was beause the teacher said I didn't stand on both feet.

Sincerely,
Leigh Botts.

November 7

Dear Mr. Henshaw,

I got your letter and did what you said. I read a different book by you. I read "Moose on Toast." I liked it almost as much as "Ways to Amuse a Dog." It was really funny the way the the boy's mother tried to think up ways to cook the moose meat they had in their freezer. 1000 pounds is a lot of moose. Mooseburgers, moose stew and moose meat loaf don't sound too bad. Maybe moose mincemeat pie would be OK because with all the raisins and junk you wouldn't know you were eating moose. Creamed chipped moose on toast, YUCK.

I don't think the boy's father should have shot the moose, but I guess there are plenty of moose up there ~~is~~ in Alaska, and maybe they needed it for food.

If my Dad shot a moose I would feed the tough parts to my dog Bandit.

Your number #1 fan,

Leigh Botts

September 20

Dear Mr. Henshaw,

This year I am in the sixth grade in a new school in a different town. Our teacher is making us do author reports to improve our writing skills, so of course I thought of you. Please answer the following questions.

1. How many books have you written?
2. Is Boyd Henshaw your real name or is it fake?
3. Why do you write books for children?
4. Where do you get your ideas?
5. Do you have any kids?
6. What is your favourite book that you wrote.
7. Do you like to write books?
8. What is the title of your next book?
9. What is your favourite animal?
10. Please give me some tips on how to write a book.

This is important to me. I really want to know so I can get to be a famous author and write books exactly like yours.

Please send me a list of your books that you wrote, an autographed picture and a bookmark. I need your answer by next Friday. This is urgent.

Sincerely,
Leigh Botts

I Getter De Madder De Letter De Later De

De Liver De Letter De Sooner De Better

Last One into Bed

by Michael Rosen

"Last one into bed
has to switch out the light."
It's just the same every night.
There's a race.
I'm ripping off my trousers and shirt—
he's kicking off his shoes and socks.

"My sleeve's stuck."
"This button's too big for its button-hole."
"Have you hidden my pyjamas?"
"Keep your hands off mine."
If you win
you get where it's safe
before the darkness comes—
but if you lose
if you're last
you know what you've got coming up is
the journey from the light switch
to your bed.
It's the Longest Journey in the World.

"You're last tonight," my brother says.
And he's right.
There is nowhere so dark
as that room in the moment
after I've switched out the light.

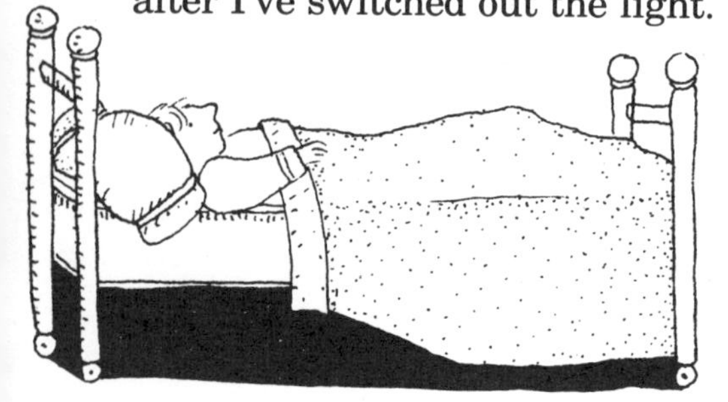

There is nowhere so full of dangerous things—
things that love dark places—
things that breathe only when you breathe
and hold their breath when I hold mine.
So I have to say:
"I'm not scared."
That face, grinning in the pattern on the wall
isn't a face—
"I'm not scared."
That prickle on the back of my neck
is only the label on my pyjama jacket—
"I'm not scared."
That moaning-moaning is nothing
but water in a pipe—
"I'm not scared."

Everything's going to be just fine
as soon as I get into that bed of mine.
Such a terrible shame
it's always the same
it takes so long
it takes so long
it takes so long
to get there.

From the light switch
to my bed.
It's the Longest Journey in the World.

The Itch

by Michael Rosen

If your hands get wet
in the washing-up water,
if they get covered in flour,
if you get grease or oil
all over your fingers,
if they land up in the mud,
wet grit, paint, or glue . . .

have you noticed
it's just then
that you always get
a terrible itch
just inside your nose?

And you can try to
twitch your nose,
twist your nose,
squeeze your nose,
scratch it with your arm,
scrape your nose on
your shoulder
or press it
up against the wall,

but it's no good.
You can't get rid of
the itch.
It drives you so mad
you just have to let a
finger get at it.

And before you know
you've done it,
you've wiped a load of glue,
or oil,
or cold wet pastry
all over the end of your nose.

The Doughnuts

by Robert McCloskey

One Friday night in November Homer overheard his mother talking on the telephone to Aunt Agnes over in Centerburg. "I'll stop by with the car in about half an hour and we can go to the meeting together," she said, because tonight was the night the Ladies' Club was meeting to discuss plans for a box social and to knit and sew for the Red Cross.

"I think I'll come along and keep Uncle Ulysses company while you and Aunt Agnes are at the meeting," said Homer.

So after Homer had combed his hair and his mother had looked to see if she had her knitting instructions and the right size needles, they started for town.

Homer's Uncle Ulysses and Aunt Agnes have a very up and coming lunch room over in Centerburg, just across from the court house on the town square. Uncle Ulysses is a man with advanced ideas and a weakness for labour saving devices. He equipped the lunch room with automatic toasters, automatic coffee maker, automatic dish washer, and an automatic doughnut maker. All just the latest thing in labour saving devices. Aunt Agnes would throw up her hands and sigh every time Uncle Ulysses bought a new labour saving device. Sometimes she became unkindly disposed toward him for days and days. She was of the opinion that Uncle Ulysses just frittered away his spare time over at the barber shop with the sheriff and the boys, so, what was the good of a labour saving device that gave you more time to fritter?

When Homer and his mother got to Centerburg they stopped at the lunch room, and after Aunt Agnes had come out and said, "My, how that boy does grow!" which was what she always said, she went off with Homer's mother in the car. Homer went into the lunch room and said, "Howdy, Uncle Ulysses!"

"Oh, hello, Homer. You're just in time," said Uncle Ulysses. "I've been going over this automatic doughnut machine, oiling the machinery and cleaning the works . . . wonderful things, these labour saving devices."

"Yep," agreed Homer, and he picked up a cloth and started polishing the metal trimmings while Uncle Ulysses tinkered with the inside workings.

"Opfwo-oof!!" sighed Uncle Ulysses and, "Look here, Homer, you've got a mechanical mind. See if you can find where these two pieces fit in. I'm going across to the barber shop for a spell, 'cause there's somethin' I've got to talk to the sheriff about. There won't be much business here until the double feature is over and I'll be back before then."

Then as Uncle Ulysses went out the door he said, "Uh, Homer, after you get the pieces in place, would you mind mixing up a batch of doughnut batter and putting it in the machine? You could turn the switch and make a few doughnuts to have on hand for the crowd after the movie . . . if you don't mind."

"O.K." said Homer, "I'll take care of everything."

A few minutes later a customer came in and said, "Good evening, Bud."

Homer looked up from putting the last piece in the doughnut machine and said, "Good evening, Sir, what can I do for you?"

"Well, young feller, I'd like a cup o' coffee and some doughnuts," said the customer.

"I'm sorry, Mister, but we won't have any doughnuts for about half an hour, until I can mix some dough and start this machine. I could give you some very fine sugar rolls instead."

"Well, Bud, I'm in no real hurry so I'll just have a cup o' coffee and wait around a bit for the doughnuts. Fresh doughnuts are always worth waiting for is what I always say."

"O.K.," said Homer, and he drew a cup of coffee from Uncle Ulysses' super automatic coffee maker.

"Nice place you've got here," said the customer.

"Oh, yes," replied Homer, "this is a very up and coming lunch room with all the latest improvements."

"Yes," said the stranger, "must be a good business. I'm in business too. A travelling man in outdoor advertising. I'm a sandwich man, Mr. Gabby's my name."

"My name is Homer. I'm glad to meet you, Mr. Gabby. It must be a fine profession, travelling and advertising sandwiches."

"Oh no," said Mr. Gabby, "I don't advertise sandwiches, I just wear any kind of an ad, one sign on front and one sign on behind, this way . . . Like a sandwich. Ya know what I mean?"

"Oh, I see. That must be fun, and you travel too?" asked Homer as he got out the flour and the baking powder.

"Yeah, I ride the rods between jobs, on freight trains, ya know what I mean?"

"Yes, but isn't that dangerous?" asked Homer.

"Of course there's a certain amount a' risk, but you take any method a' travel these days, it's all dangerous. Ya know what I mean? Now take airplanes for instance . . . "

Just then a large shiny black car stopped in front of the lunch room and a chauffeur helped a lady out of the rear door. They both came inside and the lady smiled at Homer and said, "We've stopped for a light snack. Some doughnuts and coffee would be simply marvelous."

Then Homer said, "I'm sorry, Ma'm, but the doughnuts won't be ready until I make this batter and start Uncle Ulysses' doughnut machine."

"Well now aren't *you* a clever young man to know how to make *doughnuts!*"

"Well," blushed Homer, "I've really never done it before but I've got a receipt to follow."

"Now, young man, you simply must allow me to help. You know, I haven't made doughnuts for years, but I know the best receipt for doughnuts. It's marvelous, and we really must use it."

"But, Ma'am . . . " said Homer.

"Now just *wait* till you taste these doughnuts," said the lady. "Do you have an apron?" she asked, as she took off her fur coat and her rings and her jewellery and rolled up her sleeves. "Charles," she said to the chauffeur, "hand me that baking powder, that's right, and, young man, we'll need some nutmeg."

So Homer and the chauffeur stood by and handed things and cracked the eggs while the lady mixed and stirred. Mr. Gabby sat on his stool, sipped his coffee, and looked on with great interest.

"There!" said the lady when all of the ingredients were mixed. "Just *wait* till you taste these doughnuts!"

"It looks like an awful lot of batter," said Homer as he stood on a chair and poured it into the doughnut machine with the help of the chauffeur. "It's about *ten* times as much as Uncle Ulysses ever makes."

"But wait till you taste them!" said the lady with an eager look and a smile.

Homer got down from the chair and pushed a button on the machine marked START. Rings of batter started dropping into the hot fat. After a ring of batter was cooked on one side an automatic gadget turned it over and the other side would cook. Then another automatic gadget gave the doughnut a little push and it rolled neatly down a little chute, all ready to eat.

"That's a simply *fascinating* machine," said the lady as she waited for the first doughnut to roll out.

"Here, young man, *you* must have the first one. Now isn't that just *too* delicious!? Isn't it simply marvelous?"

"Yes, Ma'm, it's very good," replied Homer as the lady handed doughnuts to Charles and to Mr. Gabby and asked if they didn't think they were simply divine doughnuts.

"It's an old family recipe!" said the lady with pride.

Homer poured some coffee for the lady and her chauffeur and

OUR

for Mr. Gabby, and a glass of milk for himself. Then they all sat down at the lunch counter to enjoy another few doughnuts apiece.

"I'm so glad you enjoy my doughnuts," said the lady. "But now, Charles, we really must be going. If you will just take this apron, Homer, and put two dozen doughnuts in a bag to take along, we'll be on our way. And, Charles, don't forget to pay the young man." She rolled down her sleeves and put on her jewellery, then Charles managed to get her into her big fur coat.

"Good night, young man, I haven't had so much fun in years. I *really* haven't!" said the lady, as she went out the door and into the big shiny car.

"Those are sure good doughnuts," said Mr. Gabby as the car moved off.

"You bet!" said Homer. Then he and Mr. Gabby stood and watched the automatic doughnut machine make doughnuts.

After a few dozen more doughnuts had rolled down the little chute, Homer said, "I guess that's about enough doughnuts to sell to the after theater customers. I'd better turn the machine off for a while."

Homer pushed the button marked STOP and there was a little click, but nothing happened. The rings of batter kept right on dropping into the hot fat, and an automatic gadget kept right on turning them over, and another automatic gadget kept right on giving them a little push and the doughnuts kept right on rolling down the little chute, all ready to eat.

"That's funny," said Homer, "I'm sure that's the right button!" He pushed it again but the automatic doughnut maker kept right on making doughnuts.

"Well I guess I must have put one of those pieces in backwards," said Homer.

"Then it might stop if you pushed the button marked START," said Mr. Gabby.

Homer did, and the doughnuts still kept rolling down the little chute, just as regular as a clock can tick.

"I guess we could sell a few more doughnuts," said Homer, "but

I'd better telephone Uncle Ulysses over at the barber shop." Homer gave the number and while he waited for someone to answer he counted thirty-seven doughnuts roll down the little chute.

Finally someone answered "Hello!" This is the sarber bhop, I mean the barber shop."

"Oh, hello, sheriff. This is Homer. Could I speak to Uncle Ulysses?"

"Well, he's playing pinochle right now," said the sheriff. "Anythin' I can tell 'im?"

"Yes," said Homer. "I pushed the button marked STOP on the doughnut machine but the rings of batter keep right on dropping into the hot fat, and an automatic gadget keeps right on turning them over, and another automatic gadget keeps giving them a little push, and the doughnuts keep right on rolling down the little chute! It won't stop!"

"O.K. Wold the hire, I mean, hold the wire and I'll tell 'im." Then Homer looked over his shoulder and counted another twenty-one doughnuts roll down the little chute, all ready to eat. Then the sheriff said, "He'll be right over. . . . Just gotta finish this hand."

"That's good," said Homer. "G'by, sheriff."

The window was full of doughnuts by now so Homer and Mr. Gabby had to hustle around and start stacking them on plates and trays and lining them up on the counter.

"Sure are a lot of doughnuts!" said Homer.

"You bet!" said Mr. Gabby. "I lost count at twelve hundred and two and that was quite a while back."

People had begun to gather outside the lunch room window, and someone was saying, "There are almost as many doughnuts as there are people in Centerburg, and I wonder how in tarnation Ulysses thinks he can sell all of 'em!"

Every once in a while somebody would come inside and buy some, but while somebody bought two to eat and a dozen to take home, the machine made three dozen more.

By the time Uncle Ulysses and the sheriff arrived and pushed through the crowd, the lunch room was a calamity of doughnuts! Doughnuts in the window, doughnuts piled high on the shelves,

doughnuts stacked on plates, doughnuts lined up twelve deep all along the counter, and doughnuts still rolling down the little chute, just as regular as a clock can tick.

"Hello, sheriff, hello, Uncle Ulysses, we're having a little trouble here," said Homer.

"Well, I'll be dunked!!" said Uncle Ulysses.

"Dernd ef you won't be when Aggy gits home," said the sheriff. "Mighty fine doughnuts though. What'll you do with 'em all, Ulysses?"

Uncle Ulysses groaned and said, "What will Aggy say? We'll never sell 'em all."

Then Mr. Gabby, who hadn't said anything for a long time, stopped piling doughnuts and said, "What you need is an advertising man. Ya know what I mean? You got the doughnuts, ya gotta create a market. . . . Understand? . . . It's balancing the demand with the supply. . . . That sort of thing."

"Yep!" said Homer. "Mr. Gabby's right. We have to enlarge our market. He's an advertising sandwich man, so if we hire him, he can walk up and down in front of the theater and get the customers."

"You're hired, Mr. Gabby!" said Uncle Ulysses.

Then everybody pitched in to paint the signs and to get Mr. Gabby sandwiched between. They painted "SALE ON DOUGHNUTS" in big letters on the window too.

Meanwhile the rings of batter kept right on dropping into the hot fat, and an automatic gadget kept right on turning them over, and another automatic gadget kept right on giving them a little push, and the doughnuts kept right on rolling down the little chute, just as regular as a clock can tick.

"I certainly hope this advertising works," said Uncle Ulysses, wagging his head. "Aggy'll certainly throw a fit if it don't."

The sheriff went outside to keep order, because there was quite a crowd by now—all looking at the doughnuts and guessing how many thousand there were, and watching new ones roll down the little chute, just as regular as a clock can tick. Homer and Uncle Ulysses kept stacking doughnuts. Once in a while somebody bought a few, but not very often.

Then Mr. Gabby came back and said, "Say, you know there's not much use o' me advertisin' at the theater. The show's all over, and besides almost everybody in town is out front watching that machine make doughnuts!"

"Zeus!" said Uncle Ulysses. "We must get rid of these doughnuts before Aggy gets here!"

"Looks like you will have ta hire a truck ta waul 'em ahay, I mean haul 'em away!!" said the sheriff who had just come in. Just then there was noise and a shoving out front and the lady from the shiny black car and her chauffeur came pushing through the crowd and into the lunch room.

"Oh, gracious!" she gasped, ignoring the doughnuts, "I've lost my diamond bracelet, and I know I left it here on the counter," she said, pointing to a place where the doughnuts were piled in stacks of two dozen.

"Yes, Ma'm, I guess you forgot it when you helped make the batter," said Homer.

Then they moved all the doughnuts around and looked for the

diamond bracelet, but they couldn't find it anywhere. Meanwhile the doughnuts kept rolling down the little chute, just as regular as a clock can tick.

After they had looked all around the sheriff cast a suspicious eye on Mr. Gabby, but Homer said, "He's all right, sheriff, he didn't take it. He's a friend of mine."

Then the lady said, "I'll offer a reward of one hundred dollars for that bracelet! It really *must* be found! . . . it *really* must!"

"Now don't you worry, lady," said the sheriff. "I'll get your bracelet back!"

"Zeus! This is terrible!" said Uncle Ulysses. "First all of these doughnuts and then on top of all that, a lost diamond bracelet . . . "

Mr. Gabby tried to comfort him, and he said, "There's always a bright side. That machine'll probably run outta batter in an hour or two."

If Mr. Gabby hadn't been quick on his feet Uncle Ulysses would have knocked him down, sure as fate.

Then while the lady wrung her hands and said, "We must find it, we *must!*" and Uncle Ulysses was moaning about what Aunt Agnes would say, and the sheriff was eyeing Mr. Gabby, Homer sat down and thought hard.

Before twenty more doughnuts could roll down the little chute he shouted, "SAY! I know where the bracelet is! It was lying here on the counter and got mixed up in the batter by mistake! The bracelet is cooked inside one of these doughnuts!"

"Why . . . I really believe you're right," said the lady through her tears. "Isn't that *amazing?* Simply *amazing*!"

"I'll be durn'd!" said the sheriff.

"OhH-h!" moaned Uncle Ulysses. "Now we have to break up all of these doughnuts to find it. Think of the *pieces!* Think of the *crumbs!* Think of what *Aggy* will say!"

"Nope," said Homer. "We won't have to break them up. I've got a plan."

So Homer and the advertising man took some cardboard and some paint and printed another sign. They put this sign in the window, and the sandwich man wore two more signs that said the same thing and walked around the crowd out front.

THEN . . . The doughnuts began to sell! *Everybody* wanted to buy doughnuts, *dozens* of doughnuts!

And that's not all. Everybody bought coffee to dunk the doughnuts into. Those that didn't buy coffee bought milk or soda. It kept Homer and the lady and the chauffeur and Uncle Ulysses and the sheriff busy waiting on the people who wanted to buy doughnuts.

When all but the last couple of hundred doughnuts had been sold, Rupert Black shouted, "I GAWT IT!!" and sure enough . . . there was the diamond bracelet inside of his doughnut!

Then Rupert went home with a hundred dollars, the citizens of Centreburg went home full of doughnuts, the lady and her chauffeur drove off with the diamond bracelet, and Homer went home with his mother when she stopped by with Aunt Aggy.

As Homer went out of the door he heard Mr. Gabby say, "Neatest trick of merchandising I ever seen," and Aunt Aggy was looking sceptical while Uncle Ulysses was saying, "The rings of batter kept right on dropping into the hot fat, and the automatic gadget kept right on turning them over, and the other automatic gadget kept right on giving them a little push, and the doughnuts kept right on rolling down the little chute just as regular as a clock can tick—they just kept right on a comin', an' a comin', an' a comin', an' a comin'."

Company Manners

Hands off the tablecloth
Don't rumble belly
Don't grab for grub
Don't slurp the soup
Don't crumble the crackers
Don't mash the mushrooms
Don't mush the potatoes
Don't stab the steak
Don't slap the saltshaker
Don't pill the bread
Don't swill the sauce
Don't ooze the mayonnaise
Don't slop the slaw
Don't spatter the ketchup
Don't gulp the olives
Don't spit the pits
Don't finger the lettuce
Don't dribble dressing
Don't chomp the celery
Don't gobble the cobbler
Don't guzzle the fizz
Swallow, don't swig
Don't smack your lips
Pat with a napkin
Daintily dab
Quietly quaff
Fastidious sip
And gracefully sample
A nibbling tidbit.

How to Eat a Poem

Don't be polite.
Bite in.
Pick it up with your fingers and lick the juice that
    may run down your chin.
It is ready and ripe now, whenever you are.

You do not need a knife or fork or spoon
or plate or napkin or tablecloth.

For there is no core
or stem
or rind
or pit
or seed
or skin
to throw away.

Poems by Eve Merriam

by William Cole

SNEAKY BILL

I'm Sneaky Bill, I'm terrible mean and vicious,
I steal all the cashews from the mixed-nut dishes;
I eat all the icing but I won't touch the cake,
And what you won't give me, I'll go ahead and take.

I gobble up the cherries from everyone's drinks,
And whenever there are sausages I grab a dozen links;
I take both drumsticks if there's turkey or chicken,
And the biggest strawberries are what I'm pickin';

I make sure I get the finest chop on the plate,
And I'll eat the portions of anyone who's late!
I'm always on the spot before the dinner bell—
I guess I'm pretty awful,
but
I
do
eat
well!

BanANANANANANANANANAa

I thought I'd win the spelling bee
And get right to the top,
But I started to spell "banana,"
And I didn't know where to stop.

GOOD NEWS

The Board of Education has just set up new rules
That in the future they'll shut all the schools
On every April Fool's.

APRIL FOOL!
(Keep cool)

Just FOR a change

I wish that things didn't all have to be
The colours you always expect to see:

Just imagine a sky of green,
A sky that's never, ever seen;
And from it shines on everyone
A great big cheerful purple sun!

Over the grass of bright, bright red
Orange flowers and black are spread;
One other thing not seen before—
A silver house, a golden door . . .

I know it sounds silly, crazy, and strange,
But *I'd* like to see it, just for a change.

Firefly, airplane, satellite, star—
How I wonder which you are.

Can't Deny IT

Tall people sleep more than short people, it's said,
And the reason is that they're longer in bed.

Listen to the Hodja

retold by Barbara Winther

There are many hodjas in Turkey, for hodjas are teachers. Only one is called The *Hodja. Some people call The Hodja simple-minded. Others consider him wise. Listen to The Hodja, and you be the judge.*

SETTING: *A Turkish village. There are two houses open to the street which runs across the stage, so that action within the houses is visible to the audience. In* **JAMAL'S** *house, left, there is a low table set with four bowls and spoons and four pillows on the floor around it. In* **THE HODJA'S** *house, right, there is a large pillow on the floor with a tall water jar beside it. The jar is empty.*

AT RISE: **JAMAL** *is sitting on a pillow in his house.* **THE HODJA** *enters left, riding his grey* **DONKEY** *or walking beside it.* **TWO GUESTS** *are standing on the street, in front of the houses.* NOTE: *During the play, spotlights shine on each house as the action shifts.*

1ST GUEST (*calling to* **THE HODJA**): Are you going to Jamal's house for dinner?

THE HODJA: Yes! I am looking forward to it.

2ND GUEST: You had best hurry, or you will be late.

THE HODJA: I cannot insult my little grey donkey by calling him

slow. (**DONKEY** *turns head and looks at* **THE HODJA.**) I realize that it is *I* who am moving slowly, and my little grey donkey cannot make *me* go any faster. (**DONKEY** *lifts head and brays.*) I do not have time to change my old clothes. I shall have to go to the dinner just as I am. (*Turns* **DONKEY** *around and rides up to* **JAMAL'S** *house, then climbs off, pats* **DONKEY'S** *head and ties him to a post.*) Stay there and guard the house. (**DONKEY** *brays, lies down and goes to sleep.* **TWO GUESTS** *approach doorway of* **JAMAL'S** *house.* **THE HODJA** *gives one last look at* **DONKEY**, *shrugs, then goes to stand behind* **GUESTS**, *as* **JAMAL** *rises from pillow, and comes to doorway.*)

JAMAL (*to* **GUESTS**, *ignoring* **THE HODJA**): My dear friends, I am honoured that you came to my house this evening.

1ST GUEST: Your dinners are always excellent, Jamal.

2ND GUEST: And your company is exceedingly entertaining.

THE HODJA: Good evening, everyone. (*The three men turn, look appraisingly at* **THE HODJA**, *then turn away and continue talking, ignoring him.*)

JAMAL: Although I do not like to brag, I do believe that the pilaf which my wife prepares is the finest in all of Turkey. Come in.

1ST GUEST: She is a fine cook, Jamal.

2ND GUEST: My mouth waters at the mention of good food. I have not eaten since morning. (**JAMAL** *walks to table, and* **GUESTS** *and* **THE HODJA** *follow.*)

THE HODJA (*clearing throat*): Jamal, I have been out tending my grapes today. I noticed that your grapes were twice as large as mine.

JAMAL (*ignoring him, to* **GUESTS**): Let us sit down at the table. (**JAMAL** *points to pillows for* **GUESTS**.) You sit here on this side of me, and you sit here on the other side. (**JAMAL** *and* **GUESTS** *sit.*)

THE HODJA (*clearing throat louder*): Jamal. Where do you wish me to sit?

JAMAL (*ignoring him, clapping hands and calling off*): Servants! Bring the food and place it before us. (**SERVANTS** *enter left, carrying platter of meat and bowls of pilaf and pistachio nuts, which they pass to* **JAMAL** *and* **GUESTS**. **THE HODJA** *stands back, coughs, then nervously strokes his beard.* **SERVANTS** *exit.* **THE HODJA**, *as if making decision, clears throat again very loudly, then steps over to table.*)

THE HODJA: Jamal, was I not invited to dinner at your house this evening?

JAMAL (*ignoring him*): When our meal is over, honoured guests, I have an excellent dancer from Constantinople to entertain us.

GUESTS: Ah! (**THE HODJA** *looks down at his clothes, shrugs, quietly turns away and goes into street. He unties* **DONKEY**.)

THE HODJA: Up, up, little grey donkey. We are going home. (**DONKEY** *rises with much effort, braying.* **THE HODJA** *climbs on.*) Forward! (**DONKEY** *walks slowly around stage to* **THE HODJA'S** *doorway.*) Whoa! (*He climbs off, pats* **DONKEY'S** *head, and ties him to a post in front of his house.*) Now you have *my* house to guard. (**DONKEY** *brays, lies down and goes to sleep.* **THE HODJA** *shrugs, scratches his beard, thinking. Suddenly he gets idea, leaps over* **DONKEY**, *and enters doorway of his house, shouting*

excitedly.) Wife! My wife, where are you? (**WIFE** *enters right.*)

WIFE: Husband, it is late. Are you not going to the dinner at Jamal's house?

THE HODJA (*shouting*): Soap and water, wife! At once!

WIFE (*picking up jar*): Yes, husband. At once! (*Exits.*)

THE HODJA (*sitting on pillow*): All of the guests were clean and finely dressed, and I was a disgrace to behold.

WIFE (*re-entering with soap, towel, and water jar, which she gives to* **THE HODJA**): Do you wish your best turban?

THE HODJA (*washing*): Yes! And bring my handsome new coat immediately.

WIFE: Immediately! (*Exits.*)

THE HODJA (*removing shoes and calling to* **WIFE**): I have no other shoes, and these are covered with dust.

WIFE (*re-entering with turban and coat, and handing them to* **THE HODJA**): The dust will come right off. (*Bangs shoes together so that dust flies*) See? Now they are clean. (*Helps him slip on shoes and coat*) Oh, your beard is tangled, husband. (*Hands him brush.*)

THE HODJA (*brushing beard*): How do I look now, wife?

WIFE (*standing back and admiring him*): Ah! I have not seen you look so fine in years. Surely you will impress your friends.

THE HODJA (*swaggering out doorway and untying* **DONKEY**): Up, up, little grey donkey. Stand like the noble beast you are. (**DONKEY** *looks up at* **THE HODJA** *with surprise, brays, and jumps up.* **THE HODJA** *climbs up with great dignity.*) Forward! (**WIFE** *runs to window to wave as* **THE HODJA**, *nodding stiffly to her, rides down the street and crosses to* **JAMAL'S** *doorway. Meanwhile* **WIFE** *gath-*

ers up everything but pillow and exits right.) Whoa! (*Climbs off and ties* **DONKEY** *to post.*) Guard my friend's house. Since you are the donkey of a gentleman, I suggest, indeed, I insist that you do not go to sleep. (**DONKEY** *brays loudly, sits down on rear haunches and peers down street.* **THE HODJA** *swaggers through the door.*) Good evening! (**JAMAL** *and* **GUESTS** *look up, smile, and rise.* **JAMAL** *rushes over to grasp* **THE HODJA'S** *arm.*)

JAMAL: My friend, you are late. I was worried that some terrible disaster had happened to keep you away. Welcome! Welcome, my Hodja!

1ST GUEST: It is good to see you again, O great Hodja.

2ND GUEST: You will find the dinner a most delightful one, divine Hodja.

JAMAL: Sit beside me. (*To* **1ST GUEST**) Would you mind moving over so that my dear friend can sit beside me?

1ST GUEST: Of course not, seeing that it is The Hodja who will sit next to *me.* (*All sit.*)

JAMAL (*clapping hands, calling*): Servants! Bring food for The Hodja! (**SERVANTS** *enter left with food, bowing to* **THE HODJA**. *One offers pilaf.*)

THE HODJA: This is some of your wife's excellent pilaf. (*Takes a spoonful and drops it into a fold of his turban.*) Eat, turban, eat! (*Others gasp.*)

2ND GUEST (*aside, to* **JAMAL**): Look! The Hodja is putting pilaf into his turban!

JAMAL (*to* **THE HODJA**): Effendi, are you feeling well?

THE HODJA: Quite well! Do I smell some wonderful roast mutton?

(**SERVANT** *brings platter of meat.* **THE HODJA** *takes pieces of meat and stuffs them into pockets of his coat.*) Eat, coat, eat! (*Others gasp.*)

2ND GUEST (*rising to knees and whispering to* **JAMAL**): Look! The Hodja is putting the meat into his coat pockets!

JAMAL: Yes, yes, I see, but I find it hard to believe.

THE HODJA (*loudly, startling* **1ST GUEST**): And now, the pistachio nuts! Jamal, you set a tremendous table for your friends. (**SERVANT** *offers him bowl of nuts.* **THE HODJA** *takes a handful of nuts and stuffs them into his shoes.*) Eat, shoes, eat! (**GUESTS** *gasp.*)

JAMAL (*rising*): This is too much. Why are you taking my good food and wasting it that way?

THE HODJA: You do not wish my turban to eat?

JAMAL: No, of course not!

THE HODJA (*rising to knees*): You do not wish my coat to eat?

JAMAL (*striding away from table*): No, of course not!

THE HODJA (*standing*): You do not wish my shoes to eat?

GUESTS: No, of course not!

THE HODJA (*shrugging, looking around innocently*): When I came to this house a short time ago in my old, dirty clothes, I was ignored, and there was no place at the table for me. When I come to this house in my fine, new clothes, everyone notices me, and nothing is too good for me. Therefore, I thought it was my *clothes* you had invited to dinner. Certainly, it could not have been *me*. (*All look at each other in amazement. Quick blackout and* **CURTAIN**.)

TALES OF THE HODJA

retold by Charles Downing

The Hodja was walking home when a man came up behind him and gave him a thump on the back of the head. When the Hodja turned round, the man began to apologize, saying that he had taken him for a friend of his. The Hodja, however, was very angry at this assault upon his dignity and dragged the man off to the court. It happened, however, that his assailant was a close friend of the *cadi*, and after listening to the two parties in the dispute, the *cadi* said to his friend:

"You are in the wrong. You shall pay the Hodja a farthing damages."

His friend said he had not that amount of money on him, and went off, saying he would fetch it.

Hodja waited and waited, and still the man did not return. When an hour had passed, the Hodja got up and gave the *cadi* a mighty thump on the back of his head.

"I can wait no longer," he said. "When he comes, the farthing is yours."

Once the Hodja borrowed a large cauldron from his neighbour, and when some time had passed, he placed a small metal coffee-can in it and took it back to its owner.

"What is that?" said the latter, pointing to the small can.

"Oh, your cauldron gave birth to that while it was in my possession."

The neighbour was delighted, and took both the cauldron and the coffee-can.

Some days later, the Hodja again asked his neighbour to lend him his cauldron, which he did. This time a few weeks passed, and when the neighbour felt he could do without his cauldron no longer, he went to the Hodja, and asked him to return it.

"I cannot," replied the Hodja. "Your cauldron has died."

"Died?" cried the neighbour. "How can a cauldron die?"

"Where is the difficulty?" said the Hodja. "You believed it could give birth. Why will you not believe it can die?"

One evening a guest came to stay with the Hodja, and a bed was prepared for him in the Hodja's room. In the middle of the night, the guest said to the Hodja:

"Effendi, there is a candle on the right side of your bed. Please hand it to me so that I can light it."

"Have you gone mad?" said the Hodja. "How can I tell my right from my left in the dark?"

One summer afternoon the Hodja was asleep on the verandah when he dreamed that a stranger promised him ten pieces of gold. The stranger placed them into the Hodja's palm one by one until he reached the tenth piece, with which he seemed hesitant to part.

"What are you waiting for?" said the Hodja. "You promised me ten."

At that very moment he woke up, and saw that his palm was empty. He quickly shut his eyes again, and stretched out his hand.

"All right," he said, "I'll settle for nine!"

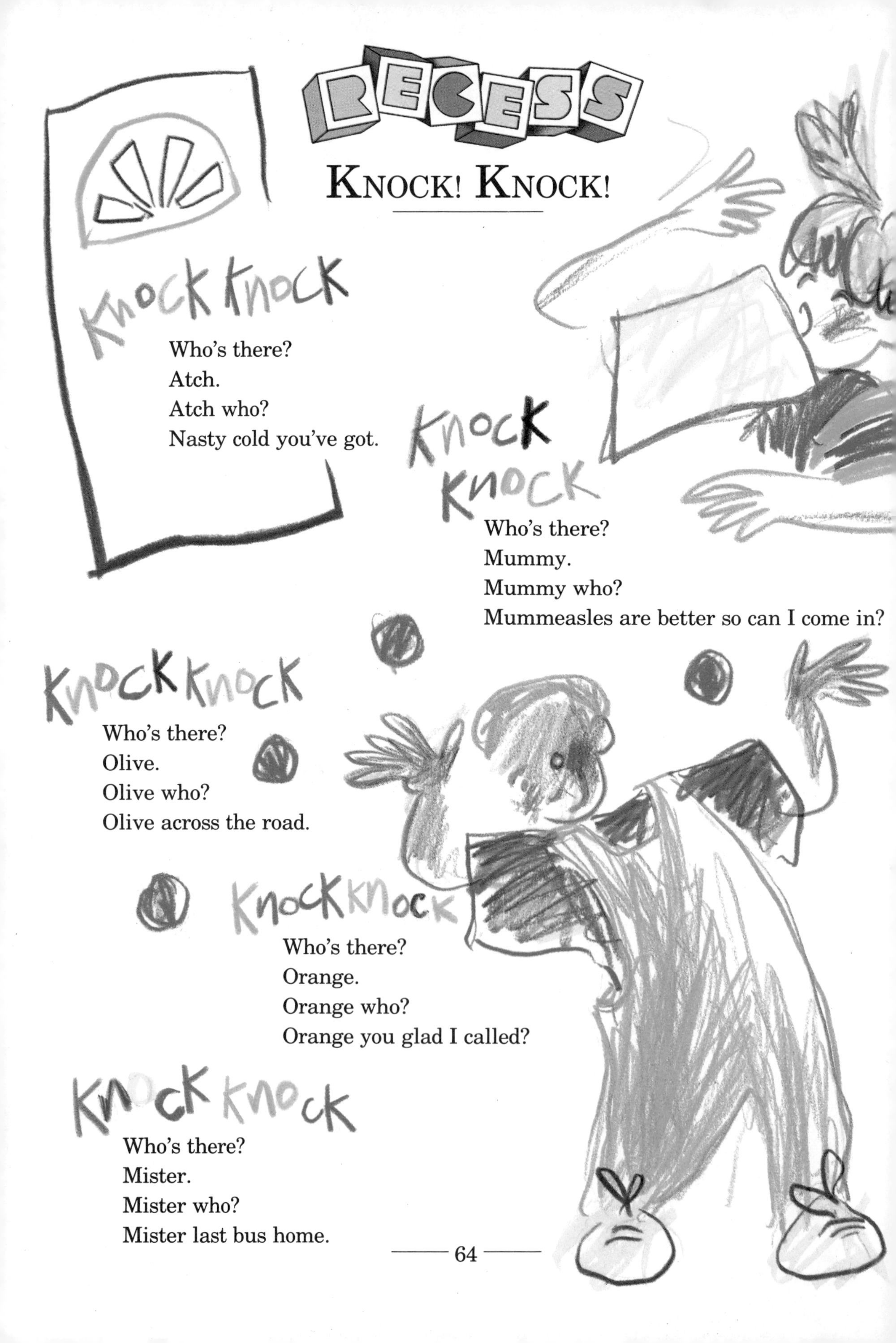

KNOCK! KNOCK!

Who's there?
Atch.
Atch who?
Nasty cold you've got.

Who's there?
Mummy.
Mummy who?
Mummeasles are better so can I come in?

Who's there?
Olive.
Olive who?
Olive across the road.

Who's there?
Orange.
Orange who?
Orange you glad I called?

Who's there?
Mister.
Mister who?
Mister last bus home.

Who's there?
Lettuce.
Lettuce who?
Lettuce in, won't you?

Who's there?
York.
York who?
York coming over to our place.

Who's there?
Alison.
Alison who?
Alison to my radio in the mornings.

Who's there?
Harry.
Harry who?
Harry up and let me in!

Who's there?
Isabel.
Isabel who?
Isabel broken? I had to knock!

Who's there?
Hurd my.
Hurd my who?
Hurd my hand so I can't knock.

Out at Night

Why do so many scary movies and books take place at night, in the dark, with only the full moon to light up the danger?

Adventure and mystery stories let you journey into places and problems that would never be part of your real life, but allow you to be part of the excitement for as long as the story lasts.

Of course, there are mysteries in everyone's life at some time, and we all have the chance to be honorary detectives. Wouldn't it be fun to be Harriet the Spy?!

Her spy clothes consisted first of all of an ancient pair of blue jeans, so old that her mother had forbidden her to wear them, but which Harriet loved because she had fixed up the belt with hooks to carry her spy tools. Her tools were a flashlight, in case

she were ever out at night, which she never was, a leather pouch for her notebook, another leather case for extra pens, a water canteen, and a boy scout knife which had, among other features, a screwdriver and a knife and fork which collapsed. She had never had occasion to eat anywhere, but someday it might come in handy.

(from *Harriet the Spy*, by Louise Fitzhugh)

Do you think that Harriet's spy kit would be effective? What would you add to it?

Perhaps it's safer to be in the middle of the action simply by using your imagination. You can be "out at night" in the middle of the day.

from
HARRIET THE SPY

by Louise Fitzhugh

"Harriet." The back door slammed and Ole Golly marched squarely toward them across the yard. Her long black shoes made a slap-slap noise on the brick.

"Hey, where are you going?" asked Harriet, jumping up. Because Ole Golly had on her outdoor things. Ole Golly just had indoor things and outdoor things. She never wore anything as recognizable as a skirt, a jacket, or a sweater. She just had yards and yards of tweed which enveloped her like a lot of discarded blankets, which ballooned out when she walked, and which she referred to as her Things.

"I'm going to take you somewhere. It's time you began to see the world. You're eleven years old and it's time you saw something." She stood there above them, so tall that when they looked up they saw the blue sky behind her head.

Harriet felt a twinge of guilt because she had seen a lot more than Ole Golly thought she had. But all she said was, "Oh, boy," and jumped up and down.

"Get your coat and hurry. We're leaving right now." Ole Golly always did everything right now. "Come on, Sport, it won't hurt you to look around too."

"I have to be back at seven to cook dinner." Sport jumped up as he said this.

"We'll be back long before that. Harriet and I eat at six. Why do you eat so late?"

"He has cocktails first. I have olives and peanuts."

"That's nice. Now go get your coats."

Sport and Harriet ran through the back door, slamming it behind them.

"What's all the noise?" spluttered the cook, who whirled around just in time to see them fly through the kitchen door and up the back stairs. Harriet's room was at the top of the house, so they had three flights to run up and they were breathless by the time they got there.

"Where're we going?" Sport shouted after Harriet's flying feet.

"I don't know," Harriet panted as they entered her room, "but Ole Golly always has good places."

Sport grabbed his coat and was out the door and halfway down the steps when Harriet said, "Wait, wait, I can't find my notebook."

"Oh, whadya need that for?" Sport yelled from the steps.

"I never go anywhere without it," came the muffled answer.

"Aw, come on, Harriet." There were great crashing noises coming from the bedroom. "Harriet? Did you fall down?"

A muffled but very relieved voice came out. "I found it. It must have slipped behind the bed." And Harriet emerged clutching a green composition book.

"You must have a hundred of them now," Sport said as they went down the steps.

"No, I have fourteen. This is number fifteen. How could I have a hundred? I've only been working since I was eight, and I'm only eleven now. I wouldn't even have this many except at first I wrote so big my regular route took almost the whole book."

"You see the same people every day?"

"Yes. This year I have the Dei Santi family, Little Joe Curry, the Robinsons, Harrison Withers, and a new one, Mrs. Plumber. Mrs. Plumber is the hardest because I have to get in the dumbwaiter."

"Can I go with you sometime?"

"No, silly. Spies don't go with friends. Anyway, we'd get caught if there were two of us. Why don't you get your own route?"

"Sometimes I watch out my window a window across the way."

"What happens there?"

"Nothing. A man comes home and pulls the shade down."

"That's not very exciting."

"It sure isn't."

They met Ole Golly waiting for them, tapping her foot, outside the front door. They walked to Eighty-sixth Street, took the cross-town bus, and soon were whizzing along in the subway, sitting in a line—Ole Golly, then Harriet, then Sport. Ole Golly stared straight ahead. Harriet was scribbling furiously in her notebook.

"What are you writing?" Sport asked.

"I'm taking notes on all those people who are sitting over there."

"Why?"

"Aw, Sport"—Harriet was exasperated—"because I've *seen* them and I want to *remember* them." She turned back to her book and continued her notes:

MAN WITH ROLLED WHITE SOCKS, FAT LEGS. WOMAN WITH ONE CROSS-EYE AND A LONG NOSE. HORRIBLE LOOKING LITTLE BOY AND A FAT BLONDE MOTHER WHO KEEPS WIPING HIS NOSE OFF. FUNNY LADY LOOKS LIKE A TEACHER AND IS READING. I DON'T THINK I'D LIKE TO LIVE WHERE ANY OF THESE PEOPLE LIVE OR DO THE THINGS THEY DO. I BET THAT LITTLE BOY IS SAD AND CRIES A LOT. I BET THAT LADY WITH THE CROSS-EYE LOOKS IN THE MIRROR AND JUST FEELS TERRIBLE.

Ole Golly leaned over and spoke to them. "We're going to Far

Rockaway. It's about three stops from here. I want you to see how this person lives, Harriet. This is *my* family."

Harriet almost gasped. She looked up at Ole Golly in astonishment, but Ole Golly just stared out the window again. Harriet continued to write:

THIS IS INCREDIBLE. COULD OLE GOLLY HAVE A FAMILY? I NEVER THOUGHT ABOUT IT. HOW COULD OLE GOLLY HAVE A MOTHER AND FATHER? SHE'S TOO OLD FOR ONE THING AND SHE'S NEVER SAID ONE WORD ABOUT THEM AND I'VE KNOWN HER SINCE I WAS BORN. ALSO SHE DOESN'T GET ANY LETTERS. THINK ABOUT THIS. THIS MIGHT BE IMPORTANT.

They came to their stop and Ole Golly led them off the subway.

"Gee," said Sport as they came up onto the sidewalk, "we're near the ocean." And they could smell it, the salt, and even a wild soft spray which blew gently across their faces, then was gone.

"Yes," said Ole Golly briskly. Harriet could see a change in her. She walked faster and held her head higher.

They were walking down a street that led to the water. The houses, set back from the sidewalk with a patch of green in front, were built of yellow brick interspersed with red. It wasn't very pretty, Harriet thought, but maybe they liked their houses this way, better than those plain red brick ones in New York.

Ole Golly was walking faster and looking sterner. She looked as though she wished she hadn't come. Abruptly she turned in at a sidewalk leading to a house. She strode relentlessly up the steps, never looking back, never saying a word. Sport and Harriet followed, wide-eyed, up the steps to the front door, through the front hall, and out the back door.

She's lost her mind, Harriet thought. She and Sport looked at each other with raised eyebrows. Then they saw that Ole Golly was heading for a small private house which sat in its own garden behind the apartment house. Harriet and Sport stood still, not knowing what to do. This little house was like a house in the country, the kind Harriet saw when she went to Water Mill in the summer. The unpainted front had the same soft grey of driftwood, the roof a darker grey.

"Come on, chickens, let's get us a hot cup of tea." Ole Golly, suddenly gay, waved from the funny little rotting porch.

Harriet and Sport ran toward the house, but stopped cold when the front door opened with a loud swish. There, suddenly, was the largest woman Harriet had ever seen.

"Why, lookahere what's coming," she bellowed, "looka them lil rascals," and her great fat face crinkled into large cheerful lumps as her mouth split to show a toothless grin. She let forth a high burbling laugh.

Sport and Harriet stood staring, their mouths open. The fat lady stood like a mountain, her hands on her hips, in a flowered cotton print dress and enormous hanging coat sweater. Probably the biggest sweater in the world, thought Harriet; probably the biggest pair of shoes too. And her shoes were a wonder. Long, long, black, bumpy things with high, laced sides up to the middle of the shin, bulging with the effort of holding in those ankles, their laces splitting them into grins against the white of the socks below. Harriet fairly itched to take notes on her.

"Wherecha get these lil things?" Her cheer rang out all over the neighbourhood. "This the lil Welsch baby? That her brother?"

Sport giggled.

"No, it's my husband," Harriet shouted.

Ole Golly turned a grim face. "Don't be snarky, Harriet, and don't think you're such a wit either."

The fat lady laughed, making her face fall in lumps again. She looks like dough, Harriet thought, about to be made into a big round Italian loaf. She wanted to tell Sport this, but Ole Golly was leading them in, all of them squeezing past that mountain of a stomach because the fat lady stood, rather stupidly, in the doorway.

Ole Golly marched to the teakettle and put a fire under it. Then she turned in a businesslike way and introduced them. "Children, this is my mother, Mrs. Golly. Mother—you can close the door now, Mother. This is Harriet Welsch."

"Harriet M. Welsch," Harriet corrected.

"You know perfectly well you have no middle name, but if you insist, Harriet M. Welsch. And this is Sport. What's your last name, Sport?"

"Rocque. Simon Rocque." He pronounced it Rock.

"Simon, Simon, hee, hee, hee." Harriet felt very ugly all of a sudden.

"You are not to make fun of anyone's name." Ole Golly loomed over Harriet and it was one of those times when Harriet knew she meant it.

"I take it back," Harriet said quickly.

"That's better." Ole Golly turned away cheerfully. "Now let's all sit down and have some tea."

"Waal, ain't she a cute lil thing." Harriet could see that Mrs. Golly was still hung up on the introductions. She stood like a mountain, her big ham hands dangling helplessly at her sides.

"Sit down, Mother," Ole Golly said gently, and Mrs. Golly sat.

Harriet and Sport looked at each other. The same thought was occurring to both of them. This fat lady wasn't very bright.

Mrs. Golly sat to the left of Harriet. She leaned over Harriet, in fact, and looked directly into her eyes. Harriet felt like something in a zoo.

"Now, Harriet, look around you," Ole Golly said sternly as she poured the tea. "I brought you here because you've never seen the inside of a house like this. Have you ever seen a house that has one bed, one table, four chairs, and a bathtub in the kitchen?"

Harriet had to move her chair back to see around Mrs. Golly, who leaned toward her, motionless, still looking. The room was a strange one. There was a sad little rug next to the stove. Harrison Withers has only a bed and a table, Harriet thought to herself. But since she didn't want Ole Golly to know she had been peering through Harrison Withers' skylight, she said nothing.

"I didn't think you had," said Ole Golly. "Look around. And drink your tea, children. You may have more milk and sugar if I haven't put enough."

"I don't drink tea," Sport said timidly.

Ole Golly shot an eye at him. "What do you mean you don't drink tea?"

"I mean I never have."

"You mean you've never tasted it?"

"No," said Sport and looked a little terrified.

Harriet looked at Ole Golly. Ole Golly wore an arch expression which signified that she was about to quote.

" 'There are few hours in life more agreeable than the hour dedicated to the ceremony known as afternoon tea.' " Ole Golly said this steadily and sedately, then leaned back in her chair with a satisfied look at Sport. Sport looked completely blank.

"Henry James," said Ole Golly, "1843–1916. From *Portrait of a Lady.*"

"What's that?" Sport asked Harriet.

"A novel, silly," said Harriet.

"Oh, like my father writes," said Sport, and dismissed the whole thing.

"My dotter's a smart one," mumbled Mrs. Golly, still looking straight at Harriet.

"Behold, Harriet," Ole Golly said, "a woman who never had any interest in anyone else, nor in any book, nor in any school, nor in any way of life, but has lived her whole life in this room, eating and sleeping and waiting to die."

Harriet stared at Mrs. Golly in horror. Should Ole Golly be saying these things? Wouldn't Mrs. Golly get mad? But Mrs. Golly just sat looking contentedly at Harriet. Perhaps, thought Harriet, she forgets to turn her head away from something unless she is told.

"Try it, Sport, it's good." Harriet spoke to Sport quickly in an effort to change the subject.

Sport took a sip. "It's not bad," he said weakly.

"Try everything, Sport, at least once." Ole Golly said this as though her mind weren't really on it. Harriet looked at her curiously. Ole Golly was acting very strangely indeed. She seemed . . . was she angry? No, not angry. She seemed sad. Harriet realized with a start that it was the first time she had ever seen Ole Golly look sad. She hadn't even known Ole Golly *could* be sad.

Almost as though she were thinking the same thing, Ole Golly suddenly shook her head and sat up straight. "Well," she said brightly, "I think we have had enough tea and enough sights for one day. I think we had better go home now."

The most extraordinary thing happened next. Mrs. Golly leaped to her fat feet and threw her teacup down on the floor. "You're always leaving. You're always leaving," she screamed.

"Now, Mother," Ole Golly said calmly.

Mrs. Golly hopped around the middle of the floor like a giant doll. She made Harriet think of those balloons, blown up like people, that bounce on the end of a string. Sport giggled suddenly. Harriet felt like giggling but wasn't sure she should.

Mrs. Golly bobbed away. "Just come here to leave me again. Always leaving. Thought you'd come for good this time."

"Now, Mother," Ole Golly said again, but this time got to her feet, walked to her mother, and laid a firm hand on the bouncing shoulder. "Mother," she said gently, "you know I'll be here next week."

"Oh, that's right," said Mrs. Golly. She stopped jumping immediately and gave a big smile to Harriet and Sport.

"Oh, boy," said Sport under his breath.

Harriet sat fascinated. Then Ole Golly got them all bundled into their clothes and they were outside on the street again, having waved to a cheerful Mrs. Golly. They walked along through the darkening day.

"Boy, oh, boy" was all Sport could say.

Harriet couldn't wait to get back to her room to finish her notes.

Ole Golly looked steadily ahead. There was no expression on her face at all.

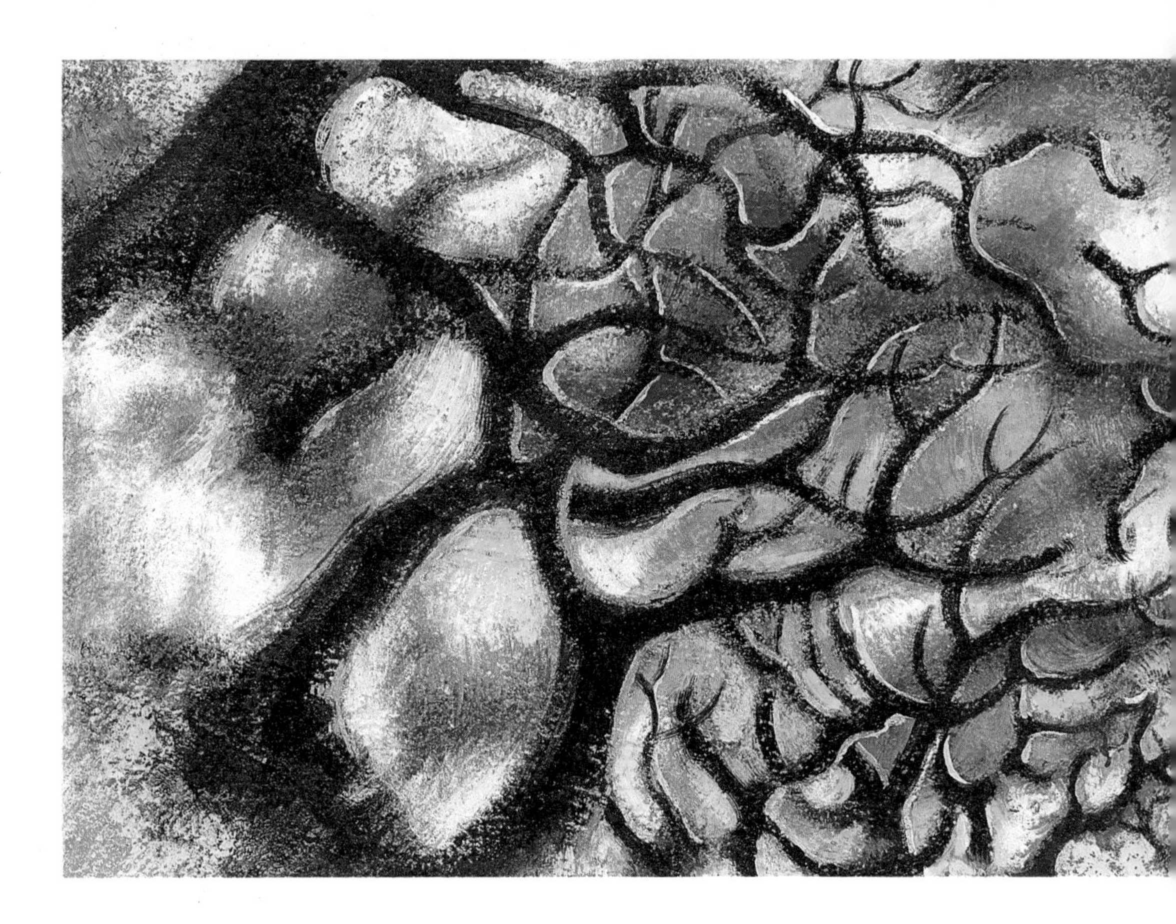

SILVER

Slowly, silently, now the moon
Walks the night in her silver shoon;
This way, and that, she peers, and sees
Silver fruit upon silver trees;
One by one the casements catch
Her beams beneath the silvery thatch;
Couched in his kennel, like a log,
With paws of silver sleeps the dog;
From their shadowy cote the white breasts peep
Of doves in a silver-feathered sleep;
A harvest mouse goes scampering by,
With silver claws, and silver eye;
And moveless fish in the water gleam,
By silver reeds in a silver stream.

The Horseman

I heard a horseman
    Ride over the hill;
The moon shone clear,
The night was still;
His helm was silver,
    And pale was he;
And the horse he rode
    Was of ivory.

Poems by Walter de la Mare

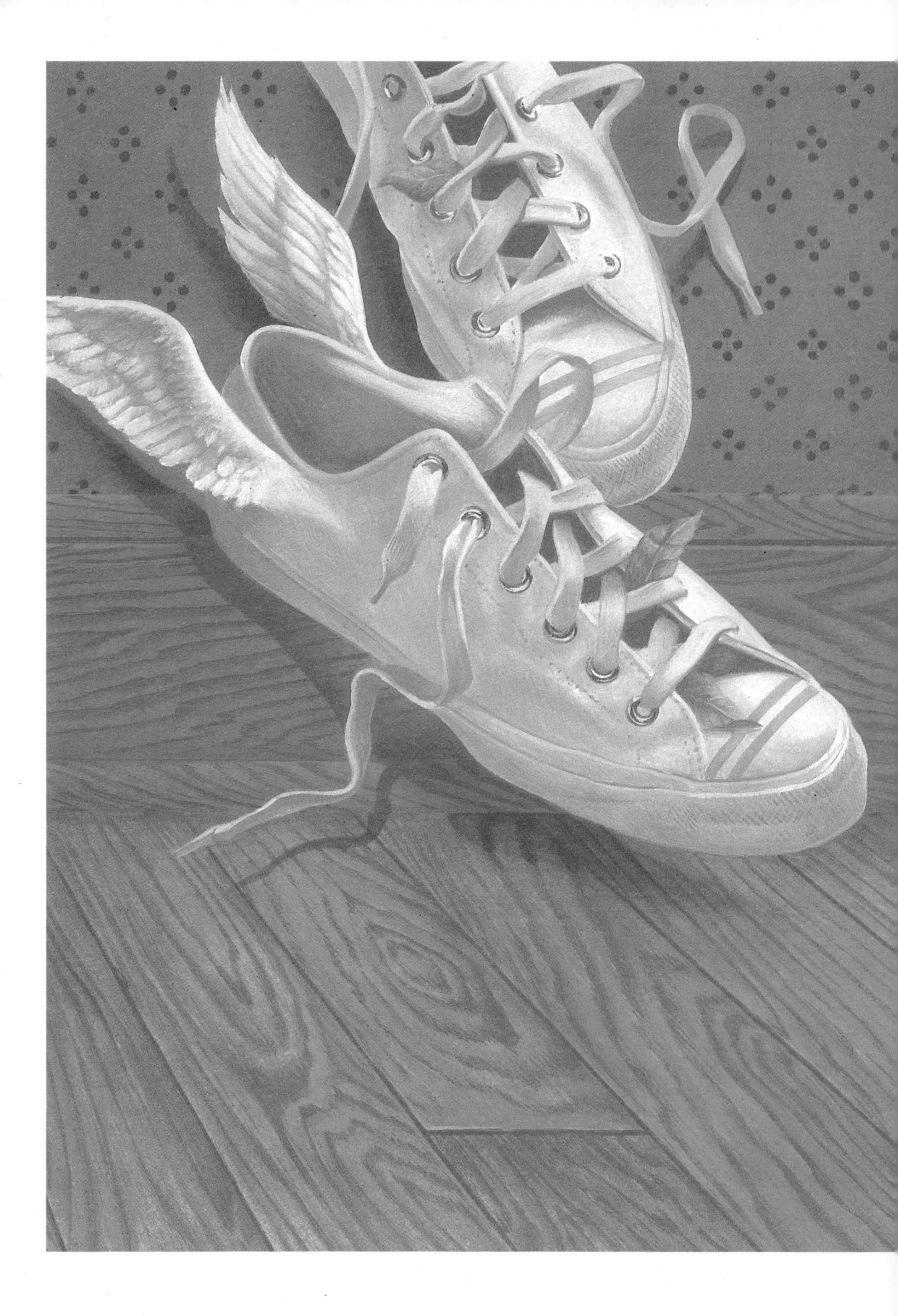

My Shoes

by Siv Cedering Fox

My shoes
are a pair
of twins
that stand by my bed
in the dark.

When I sleep
they walk
up a wall,
down a hall,
across the ceiling.

Do they open the window?
Do they open a door?
Do they run through the streets
silently?
quickly?

Do they climb up a tree
to sway on a branch?

Does a bird bring them grass
to make them a nest?

Do they borrow some wings
to fly to my room?

Do they land by my bed
with leaves in their laces

waiting for morning

and my own two
feet?

I Wonder

by Siv Cedering Fox

Sometimes when
I'm alone at night,
I think that somewhere
in the dark
someone like me
is wondering
if there is someone
just like him.

Sometimes I think
that since the moon
looks so much like
the globe of the earth,
maybe someone
could live up there,
brushing his teeth,
combing his hair,
riding his horse
across a crater,
swimming in
a lunar sea,
someone, up there, just like me.

Or somewhere further, beyond a star,
riding in his father's car,
looking up into the dark,
seeing our sun, calling it star,
there is, perhaps, a boy saying:
"I wonder
if someplace far, far away
there is a father, a mother,
a road going somewhere,
a boy and a car?"

Doug Martin

Face to Face

by Larry Swartz

Masks of all kinds hung on the walls of Aunt Rachael's apartment. Masks made of clay. Masks made of beads and shells. Masks made of magic and dreams and secrets. The masks had been collected from travels throughout the world, and behind each mask was a special memory of places once visited. Behind each mask was a story.

Once a month, Emma's parents would drop her off to visit her favourite aunt. Emma and Aunt Rachael were alike in many ways, and they always seemed to like doing the same things.

Emma's parents often warned her to stay away from her aunt's masks, but one time, when Aunt Rachael went to answer the phone, the masks seemed to beckon Emma. She stared at the masks. The masks stared back at her. "What could possibly happen?" she asked herself as she walked over to the wall.

She decided to take a risk and put on a mask, but she wasn't sure which one to choose. A mysterious, deep-brown wooden face caught her attention. The eyes were rough dramatic slits, and an open mouth showed jagged teeth that looked like the serrated edge on a package of tinfoil. Swirly scrolls etched on one cheek set off a checkerboard design on the forehead. The hair was a deadened mess of straw. Some masks were more colourful, others more amusing or bizarre, but without hesitation, Emma chose this mask to pull over her face. It was large for her eleven-year-old head, but her hand was holding it so tightly in place that she soon began to smell the wood that the mask had been carved from.

Suddenly, Emma felt very warm. Darkness filled her face. Darkness filled the room. Darkness was everywhere. And then the darkness began to grow brighter. And brighter.

Emma blinked as her eyes adjusted to the vivid white light that surrounded her. She was no longer in her aunt's apartment: where in the world was she?

She was part of a circle of people who were dressed in masks just like hers. Their arms were outstretched and they were moving together in strange dancing rhythms, moving to the beat of a drum, drum, drum. As the dancers leapt high and stamped the ground, wild cries echoed around the circle—*aweyaiooo, aweyaiooo.* The mask covering her face swept Emma, too, into the tribal ritual.

The dancers moved faster and faster. The chanting and the beating grew louder and louder. Emma felt her ears pounding. She became so frightened that she ripped the mask from her face.

Immediately, the white light vanished, the drumming stopped, and the dancing tribe disappeared.

Emma was back in the apartment. She could still hear her aunt's voice coming from the kitchen. No one would ever know what she had done. Emma went over to the wall to put the mask back where it belonged.

She looked over the display and began to wonder what other opportunities might be before her. If the primitive mask took her to a world of tribal ritual, what would happen if she tried on another? Would she once again be able to travel to another place, perhaps to another time?

Aunt Rachael's masks stared silently at Emma. She examined a white Japanese face decorated with simple black and red geometric designs. Next to it was a papier-mâché oval with hollow, ghostlike eyes, and beside that a Mexican mask bore finely painted lace de-

signs on its green surface. Shells and sticks bordered an African mask's muddy coloured features. A wolf mask splattered with colours dripped blood from its fangs. She saw a brass sun mask, a devil mask with gilded horns, an Indian corn husk mask, a carnival mask, a death mask, a futuristic mask. Masks for cures, masks for drawing away evil, masks for bringing food, masks of comedy and tragedy. All of these faced Emma.

Emma chose a birdlike half-mask made of burgundy, rust, and grey feathers that moved at a mere whisper of breath. The beak was

a small triangle of yellow leather. What harm could come from wearing this one?

As Emma tied the mask to the back of her head, a tickle slithered through her body—the feathers, she thought. When the sensation stopped, Emma was flying, fast and free. She glided on the breeze high above the earth, enjoying her flight so much that she didn't notice the weather take a sudden turn for the worse. Caught by a wind current, Emma struggled as she plunged downward. Just before she hit the ground, she brushed against a tree branch and the mask fell off. Emma, no longer a bird, found herself lying on the floor of Apartment 222.

Aunt Rachael called from the kitchen, "Are you all right?"

"Sure, I was just trying to get a book from the top shelf."

"Well, be careful! I'll just be two more minutes and then we'll go out for some lunch."

Emma rushed to try on one more mask. Without thinking, she took a plain white one from the wall. Somehow this was the most human-like of the collection, although its face had no particular expression. Emma stared at it. So many possibilities.

She put the mask on. The nose fit her nose; the mouth was the same shape as hers; the space around the eyes moulded around her eyes. Like another layer of skin, the mask fit her face perfectly. Emma began to feel suffocated, as if the mask were smothering her. She reached behind her head to undo the elastic that held the mask in place.

"Take off my mask!"

Emma's first thought was that Aunt Rachael was off the phone and scolding her for touching the masks. But was the voice her aunt's?

Emma found herself facing a girl who was wearing a mask just like her own. The girl was the same height as Emma; she had the same reddish-blond hair; even the clothes the girl was wearing matched hers. Emma could have been looking in a mirror.

"Take off my mask!" the voice repeated.

"Who are you?"

The girl didn't answer.

Emma wanted to know more about this stranger and about the mask she was wearing. It seemed that she wasn't going to get very far, but she tried another question.

"What happened to you?" Emma asked.

"Once, long ago, I put this mask on. I haven't been able to take it off since. Please free me!"

"Why can't you take it off yourself?"

"Emma, all I can tell you is that I have been hiding behind this mask for many years. There is some strange power to this mask. Take it off for me and I will give you whatever you want."

"Are you a genie?"

Again the masked girl ignored Emma's questions. "Hurry! Isn't your aunt expecting to find you in her living room?"

"How did you know about my aunt? Come to think of it, how did you know my name?"

"If I were you, I wouldn't waste any time."

"But . . ."

"Emma, don't let the same thing happen to you. Please, before it's too late, take the mask off my face."

Emma had many doubts and questions and fears. She was afraid of what would happen if she removed the stranger's mask, and was afraid, too, of meeting the face behind the mask. And if she didn't take it off? What would happen to this masked girl? Was she doomed never to change just because she touched something that didn't belong to her? Emma's fear turned to terror as she realized that *she* had put her mask on without permission. Was she to wear it forever and ever?

"Hurry, Emma, it's time for you to come face to face . . ."

Emma's mask was snapped off her face.

"What are you doing with that? Haven't you been told time and time again to leave the masks alone?" Aunt Rachael took the mask from her niece and hung it carefully back on the wall. "Won't you ever change?"

Change?

Once the mask was safely in its place, Aunt Rachael began to smile, almost to laugh. "You probably won't believe this, but once, when I was your age, I put a mask on and couldn't get it off for a long, long time. Take it from me, Emma, you have to be very careful with these masks. They are fragile pieces of art and really shouldn't be worn by anyone."

Emma looked at her aunt. Then she looked at the plain white mask on the wall and knew that the strange girl she had just met hadn't been a stranger at all.

Autumn Song of the Goose

by Jane Yolen

Rise up, rise up, my mate,
from the chilly land,
for a rich, warm smell
as subtle as a poem
rides the air
and calls us home.

Kerhonk. Kerhonk. Kerhonk.

Rise up, rise up, my friends,
from the dying land
where the headless stalks
of flowers bend
in their earthen tombs
and there are left but a few
of summer's brittle blooms.

Kerhonk. Kerhonk. Kerhonk.

The sun hangs between mountains,
the air is crisp and cold.
It is the time of flight.
Rise up, rise up, my mate, my friends,
into the piercing light.
Along the road of air
where the strong winds blow,
along the grey tunnel
lit by the pale moon,
grey sky above,
grey mud below,
and the long winds singing
their mournful old tune.
Then down to the lake
to keep our feet warm.
Nibble and shake,
nibble and shake,
a few more miles across autumn
a few more miles safe
from winter's cold alluring charm.

Kerhonk. Kerhonk. Kerhonk.

Into shallow sleep we fall,
while all about
the lullaby call
murmurs across the changing land.
Even in sleep
night whispers its warnings:
fox and stoat,
and the hunter with his gun,
blindly waiting in the early mornings.
Rise up, rise up, my friends,
and mount the singing air.
Over the changing autumn fields,
past ponds veiled in mists.
Past trackless mountains
where the trees rise up like fists.
Past houses, past towns
where small people live small lives.
It is morning, my mate,
my friends. Rise up. Rise.

Kerhonk. Kerhonk. Kerhonk.

We fly but wingtips apart,
No compass, no compass but the heart.

Kerhonk. Kerhonk. Kerhonk.

M · H · C

SASQUATCH

by Mary Hamilton

While neither a giant nor a cannibal, the Sasquatch has elements of both, combined with an almost-human quality. It is known throughout the world by a variety of names, but in Canada it is usually called "Sasquatch," which means "wild man" or "hairy man" in the Salish Indian language of the Pacific Northwest.

One of the earliest New World encounters between this creature and a European took place in British Columbia. In 1811 explorer David Thompson and his crew came upon the tracks of an animal whose footprint measured fourteen inches [35 cm] long by eight inches [20 cm] wide. Thompson's men felt certain a Sasquatch had left the huge footprint, but the explorer was less sure. At first he "held it to be the track of a large old grizzled Bear," but later he had to admit that "the shortness of the nails, the ball of the foot, and its great size was not that of a bear."

In 1882 the *Daily Colonist* reported that several residents of Yale, British Columbia, had managed to capture a Sasquatch "after considerable trouble and perilous climbing." The newspaper remarked that "since his capture, he is very reticent, only occasionally uttering a noise which is half bark and half growl."

Although there have been many more recent descriptions of this creature, one of the most dramatic was given under oath in 1955 by William Roe. He reported meeting what he first thought was a giant grizzly but soon realized was a huge female creature covered with dark-brown, silver-tipped hair. When it caught sight of Roe, "a look of amazement crossed its face." Roe continued:

> Still in a crouched position, it backed up three or four short steps, then straightened up to its full height and started to walk rapidly back the way it had come. . . . Just as it came to the other patch of bush it threw its head back and made a peculiar noise that seemed to be half laugh and half language.

The Sasquatch is a creature about which there is still a good deal of debate. Does this human-beast still wander somewhere in the depths of the British Columbia forest?

Water Monsters

by Mary Hamilton

After Christopher Columbus discovered America in 1492, explorers from various European countries sailed westward to search for new lands. As their ships crossed the perilous Atlantic, they watched for monsters of the deep, already known to them from books and hearsay.

Water serpents also found their way into rivers and lakes all over North America. Champlain saw one in the lake named after him. Since then there have been over one hundred sightings of the Lake Champlain Monster, five in 1981 alone. Recently the *New York Times* described the creature as having a "long serpentine neck" and quoted Walter Wojewodzic, a retired mine worker:

> [I saw] three grey humps about three feet [a metre] high. . . . The whole thing was about 40 feet [12 m] long. . . . It wasn't any kind of wave, fish or animal I ever saw. There's something big in that lake, awful big.

A similar creature seems to inhabit Lake Ontario. The explorer and fur trader, Pierre Esprit Radisson, reported seeing a water serpent there in 1652, and many later sightings have been recorded. An account published in the *British Whig* newspaper is typical:

> Yesterday four men, including Charles Staley and his son, went sailing and . . . had their attention directed to a peculiar looking object. . . . It was about eighteen inches [50 cm] in circumference, of an eel colour, and had a tapering head. The sight of it has created alarm.

Another variety of large serpent may inhabit western rivers and lakes. Ogopogo, or Naitaka, appears to be at home in both Okanagan Lake, British Columbia, and the waters of the North Saskatchewan River near Rocky Mountain House. Squadron leader Bruce Millar described it as "lithe and sinewy, seventy-five feet [25 m] in length, with a coiled back and a dignified demeanour."

Descriptions of a similar serpent with "cup-shaped ears" come from Utah Lake. A creature in Idaho is said to look more like a "snout-nosed crocodile."

Other lake serpents include Manipogo in Lake Manitoba, Igopogo in Lake Simcoe, Ontario, Ponik in Lake Pohenegamook, Quebec, and Le Serpent in Lake Duchêne on the Quebec-Ontario border. Unnamed creatures have also been reported from Wisconsin, Nebraska, Montana, Nevada, Oregon, California, and Vermont.

Tiger Watch

by Jan Wahl

There was trouble in the village of Onangapur.

The women who walked from the village down to the river by the melon field looked into each jungle shadow. They listened to the warning cries of the jackdaw. Afraid, they washed their clothes on the rocks.

One day, a short time ago, before the sun had set, a mother and daughter were working in a clearing where mustard plants grow. Both of them were harvesting yellow plants, cutting them with dull scythes, when something stirred in the long, soft grass.

The daughter rushed to her mother. They saw facing them, a noble-looking red tiger.

The tiger stood stock still, his whiskers trembling in the wind. Then he pounced—dragging the mother off into the jungle. A monkey howled.

The girl hurried into Onangapur. It was too late to save her mother, however. Men lit paraffin lanterns and chased after the tiger, beating pots and drums. He was gone.

No one slept well, knowing a prowling killer tiger was waiting.

The red one became bolder. In the middle of the night he tore down the bamboo fences where some white goats were tethered.

Punwa, who owned them, wept at their loss since they were his whole fortune. "I suppose I will be next!" he wailed loudly.

The village elders sat smoking hookah pipes. They voted an

eighty-rupee reward to be given to anyone who shot the tiger. They wrote it on paper. Runners took this message to other villages near and far.

Miles away, in the town of Chuka, a boy, Azad, sat on the floor of his small house, making out of wood shavings and sticks and cotton a circle of animals. Then, with a toy rifle, he pretended to stalk a black panther. Toy antelopes, an elephant, and a leopard stood nearby on wobbly legs.

"Pow!" said Azad, knocking down the panther. Putli, his mother, watched as she mended an old torn blanket.

She shook her head at the killing. "Bad enough to have one hunter in the family!" she cried.

Azad's father, Mustapha, knew how to build snares and dig pits. He was an animal catcher. Mustapha was tying a loop snare. He wore glasses, but his deep-set eyes were sharp for anything hiding in the soft grass.

There was a noise at the door—the weary runner had arrived from Onangapur.

Azad listened as his father spoke to the man, who told him about the reward of eighty rupees for hunting that sly devil, the red tiger.

Mustapha was known for hitting his mark with every shot.

"Yes, I will try," he at last told the runner. "We owe money to Mr. Punjab, and this is not the season for catching zoo and circus animals."

They shook hands. Putli gave the runner a cup of tea before he left.

Azad stood up. Plucking at his father's sleeve, he said, "Please—I have never gone with you, Father. Take me along! I might as well start now because one day I want to be as great a hunter as you."

"No," said his mother quietly. "I *wish* you to become a doctor or teacher instead."

"Listen to your mother, son," said Mustapha, checking over a battered muzzle-loading rifle.

"It is not the same as shooting a toy wood panther," warned

Putli, biting the end of her thread.

But Azad kept pleading, "Take me with you! I am *old* enough!"

"Well, Putli," said Mustapha to his wife. "Maybe the lad will learn by coming along! He must have his own gun, then."

Azad's father brought out a rusty little rifle and oiled it. Azad had already practised with it. He had shot a hawk in a meadow, on his birthday.

Silently Putli cooked them a good dinner of spinach, eggs, and rice. She turned her head away. Her small son craved to be a man and hunt a real tiger.

Mustapha, Putli, and Azad rose early, before the sun was fully up. Dew shone on poppies growing in tin cans by the door. The sky was orange-pink. Mustapha studied the roof.

"I will do this job since we owe money to Mr. Punjab and so that our roof can be repaired before the big rains pour!" he said.

Putli stood by the door watching them. They would take the river boat that carried sugar cane to Onangapur.

She called out, "And if you are both hurt? What will become of me? That tiger must be a wounded, *hungry* fellow!"

"Well," said Mustapha. "Think of eighty rupees!"

Then the boy and his father hugged Putli and soon walked out of sight.

As they passed through the village, many people in the bazaar were impressed by their guns.

Azad's eyes sparkled as he saw the many vegetable stalls, the trinkets hanging on strings, the honey, the mangos, and the new shiny guavas. He could smell cinnamon! Chili!

When they returned, he would buy some for Putli.

It was Azad's first boat ride. The boat had huge eyes painted on its prow. It was steered with long paddles and had a single sail on a tall bamboo mast.

One of the men gave Azad and his father a piece of sugar cane.

The boy sat close to Mustapha and on the journey saw shaggy black buffalos drinking at the water's edge. Later, he saw crocodile snouts and tails flashing in the river. Once they passed a sacred fig

tree, under which sat a bearded holy man.

"Oh, holy man, say us a prayer! *We hunt for tiger!*" shouted Mustapha, tossing him a coin.

The holy man saluted them. Ospreys flew low searching for river fish. The fig tree slid from view.

"Look," said Mustapha. From his bag he took an old spoon and tied a line of thread on it. He lowered the spoon to the water.

A fish rose to the surface, and then an osprey plummeted into a dive, snatched it, and flapped away in triumph.

"You see, Azad," said his father, "How quickly a living thing is caught? We will use bait for the red tiger."

The boat with painted eyes reached Onangapur, and there Azad and his father jumped off.

On the bank Mustapha shot two partridges and carried them to the elders of the village as a gift. The village itself was quiet.

Azad missed the happy sounds he heard in Chuka: the singing of his mother, for instance, when she worked!

Mustapha talked to the village elders and asked a carpenter to build a strong platform to put in a tree near the water hole.

Quickly the carpenter began his hammering.

The elders said that last night the red tiger carried off a calf that was later found at the jungle's edge jammed between some rocks. It had been partly eaten.

"I must have another bull calf for bait," instructed Mustapha.

In late afternoon, after a light meal, Azad and his father gathered their rifles and gourds of water. Four men from Onangapur walked with them into the noisy, green, hot jungle, carrying the platform on their shoulders.

When they reached the water hole, a hyena saw them and scampered off.

Nervous, the villagers helped put the platform in a wide oak, high enough so that the tiger could not reach it.

The bull calf was tethered to the tree, crying softly.

The four men boosted Azad and Mustapha up, swept away their footprints with pine branches, and left.

Mustapha broke off twigs in order to see better. Woodpeckers, magpies, and thrushes all darted past. A butterfly with bright yellow spots flashed by, and Azad would have liked to catch it.

The air was wet.

"Do not take off your shirt!" whispered Mustapha. "Light will shine on your skin." He added, "We are lucky. The moon is almost full. We will see better. But so will Tiger!"

Fuzz-fuzz flowers on the thorn trees shimmered. Slowly a porcupine scuttled through the grass and creepers. Plump spiders crawled up the oak.

Azad waited, watching the orange clay at the edge of the water hole. Mustapha did not move. The bull calf whimpered. Dusk was coming.

Suddenly a horrible howl pierced the air.

"What is it?" asked Azad, pulling at his father's sleeve. "Is that a ghost? A banshee?"

"It is the churel's cry," replied Mustapha.

"Oh," said Azad.

"Have your gun cocked. Tiger will hear the tiniest sound. Do not speak again," said his father.

So the boy kept his eyes on the calf and the water hole. The early moon was glowing bright as the sun.

A pair of jackals came to drink. Azad could see squirrels playing in the branches of a haldu tree beyond. Then a flock of grey-white pigeons burst quickly into flight. A clumsy wart hog waddled into view. It flicked its tail as if sweeping the high grass.

There was another cry. The wart hog turned.

Is it the tiger? wondered Azad. His father seemed to hear his thoughts and shook his head no. Azad must learn how to listen.

His father once said, *An owl's call is like the tiger's.*

The wart hog looked up snorting as a cobra, huge and long, slithered out of the grass. The wart hog stalked off. The cobra hissed, causing monkeys to chatter loudly.

Mustapha whispered, "Something is always awake here! Sit still. No moving or talking. Everything depends on it!"

Azad sat trying not to move. He was hungry, but the excitement made him forget it. His gun was ready, the hammer cocked, his finger on the trigger.

He remembered Mustapha telling him, *Tigers lack a sense of smell. But their ears hear everything.*

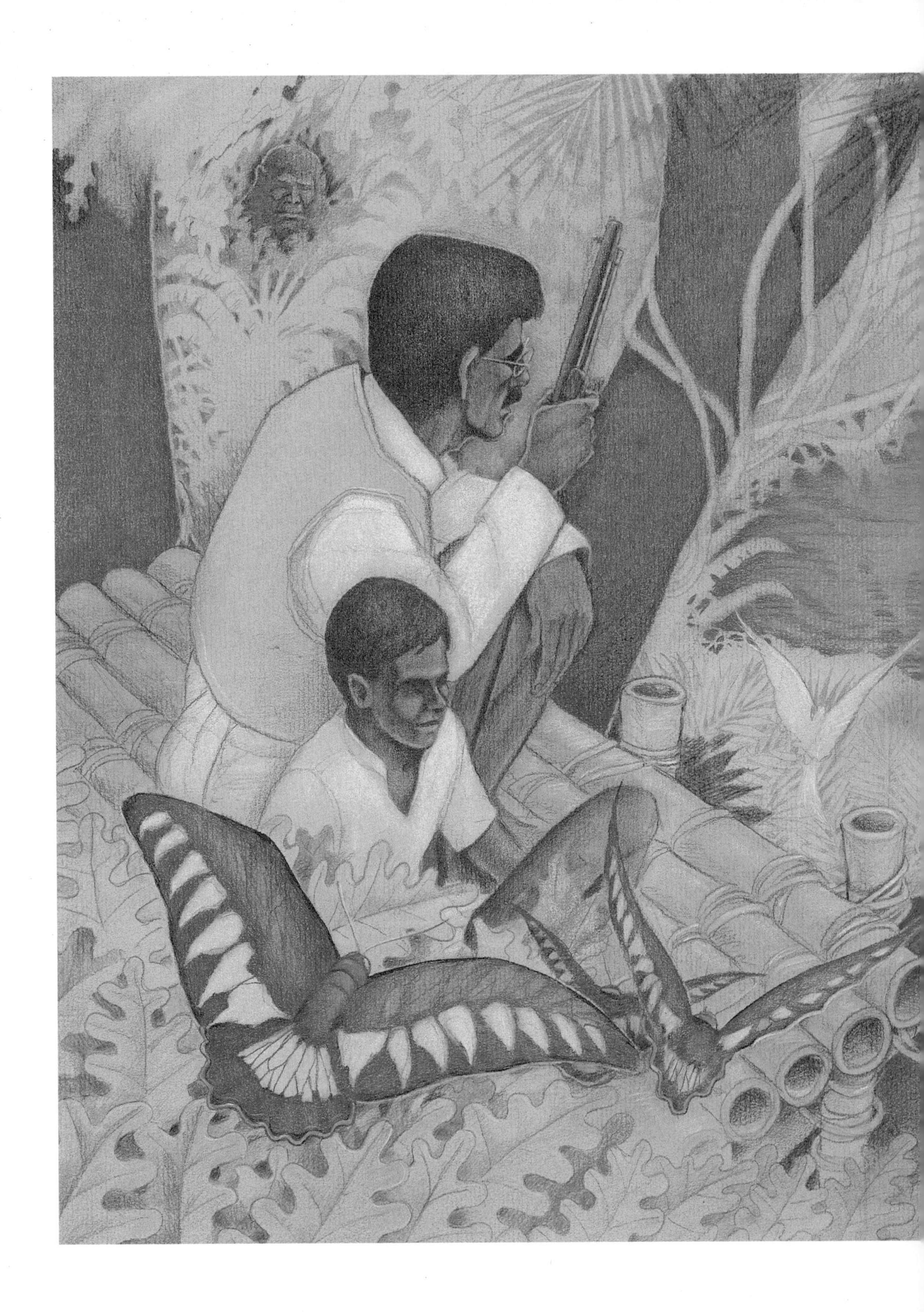

For hours Azad felt cramped but did not move. Was Putli, back at home, worrying about them? Was Mustapha sure the tiger could not leap up—clawing—to reach their platform?

In the lull of night, after staring hard, Azad saw a strange thing: a bear's head in flames, whirling round and round the oak.

I am dizzy from not sleeping, he thought. *No body! Only a head!* Azad glanced at his father and wondered if he saw it too.

As Mustapha had once said, *The jungle is a mystery.*

Below, the moonlight was now playing tricks. Each shadow seemed to be a tiger about to spring. The calf stopped whimpering.

Suddenly, straight before Azad, the tiger appeared at the water hole as if by magic.

How long had the tiger crouched there? Did Mustapha see him? Azad did not dare turn his head. How beautiful and wonderful he was! His coat was a deep red-orange and black.

He lapped water, keeping an eye on the calf. Slowly, he stretched, licking his wide chest and forepaws. Yawning. Scratching. Rolling in tangled grass by the mud. Now and then he winced as if wounded.

Azad could not shoot this great tiger. He could not! He drew his breath in astonishment.

The tiger had heard! With a simple bound the animal came to the tree. He paid no heed to the calf. He jumped toward their platform uttering a cry.

Mustapha fired both barrels of his gun. There was a great roar as the shot hit, the most terrible sound Azad had ever heard. The gun's report echoed through the jungle.

The tiger lay on his side as if only sleeping. Mustapha said, "We'll stay until morning to make sure he is dead."

Azad could not sleep. He kept staring at the tiger. The calf watched, too. Before dawn the air grew sweet and crisp, and a cool breeze blew. Finally a brilliant sun rose, and they climbed down the oak, Mustapha first.

Azad dared to touch the tiger. It was real and still warm, as warm as his own body.

"Oh, how the shot must have hurt!" he said. "How fine he looks!"

"Yes," agreed Mustapha. "Such dignity! See those porcupine quills stuck in his left foreleg and chest?"

The boy saw the wounds—tough, deep, and swollen. They counted thirty-two quills.

"Since he could not run as he once did," said Mustapha, "he became a killer of humans and defenceless animals."

Azad hung his head. Again he touched the moist, warm fur, stroking it.

When the villagers returned, they congratulated Mustapha and tied the magnificient tiger to a long stout pole.

They walked in silence, the tiger swinging on the carrier beside Azad.

Azad turned to Mustapha and said, "I do not choose to become a hunter, Father."

Mustapha took his arm. "It is well, son."

Parrots of bright colours streaked overhead. Deer raced as if waking from a dream. Monkeys chattered in the green-gold jungle.

Azad led the bull calf and walked with his father back to Onangapur, as silent as the tiger hanging upon the pole.

RUINS

by Harry Behn

Some very nice persons have no use for things
Of wind and rust and dust with wings,
Or dust that broods in the sun and sings,

But I like noons when it's hot and dusty,
And cellars that are damp and musty,
And windmills especially when they're rusty.

I like an orchard gone to seed
In thistles and gourd and tangles of weed,

I like a mossy trough that spills,
And old machinery left on hills,

Deserted barns and earthy smells,
And water shining in old wells.

I like the rumble of a warm
Cloud gathering a thunderstorm,

And gusts of wind that whirl and fall,
And stillness, and a dove's call.

Some very nice persons have no use for things
Of wind and rust and dust with wings,
Or dust that broods in the sun and sings,

But what may seem like ruins of a wall
For me hasn't changed very much at all
From the castle it was, and I hear the call

Of children who lived here long ago
Still beautiful and sunny and slow,
And the secret they know, I seem to know.

Rebus Riddles

1. Sparrow 2. Camel 3. Cat 4. Baboon 5. Swallow 6. Horse

Do you ever talk to yourself, imagining conversations that you would like to have with people who have upset you or caused you some difficulty? Often playing out these situations in your mind helps you to work through problems and to see all of the options in front of you.

Writers use their imaginations to invent strange worlds where people are caught in fantastical situations, and yet use their human brains to solve the problems. Our ancestors told folk tales, such as this Scandinavian myth about a boy who manages to outwit some fearsome trolls.

"The frost giants lived in castles of ice, surrounded by shimmering fences of northern lights. They were as wild as the mountains themselves and pelted the valleys with snow and ice—nobody dared to live in a place near them. They had more gold and silver than they knew what to do with, and hard-working gnomes were forever bringing them more. So when they were in a good mood, they would playfully toss huge balls of gold to each other. The frost giants were much bigger and stronger than you, plain trolls, and some of them had as many as five hundred heads on their shoulders. What trolls they were!"

"Tell us more," said the trolls, their mouths agape.

"Then churches were built down in the valleys and the fine

pealing of the bells hurt their rough ears so badly that they took their vast treasures and moved into the mountains."

"What then, what then?" cried the trolls, and quite forgot to look out for the rising sun.

"Well," said the boy, "don't you know that yourselves? By and by the giants faded into the past and trolls like you took over their mountain halls. You think you have all their treasures, but you are paupers compared to them. The biggest ball of gold they hid behind the mountain yonder."

"Where?" cried the trolls, and spun around. They stared straight into the golden eye of the rising sun.

With a loud crack they burst and turned to stone. One became a mountain, the other a heap of rubble. They had done what no troll must ever do. For trolls were creatures of darkness and just one glance at the sun was enough to destroy them.

(from *The Frost Giants*, by Edgar P. and Ingri D'Aulaire)

How is a mere mortal boy able to defeat the trolls? Can you think of things in your world, secret fears and worries, that you will have to fight and overcome? Perhaps imaginary stories have some relationship to the real world, and it may be that you will someday find you will have to outwit your own "trolls."

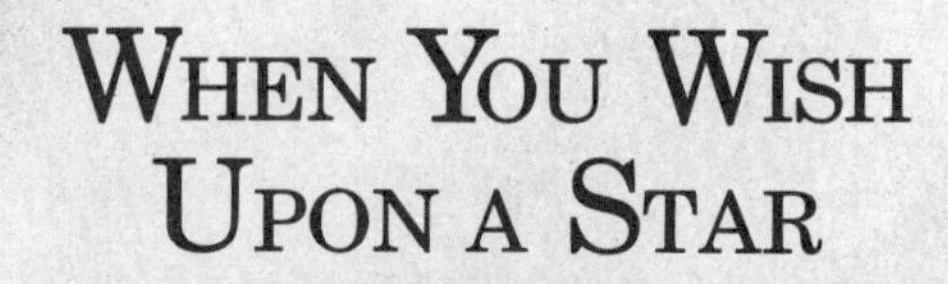

When You Wish Upon a Star

words by Ned Washington,
music by Leigh Harline

When you wish upon a star,
Makes no diff 'rence who you are,
Anything your heart desires will come to you.
If your heart is in your dream,
No request is too extreme,
When you wish upon a star as dreamers do.

Fate is kind,
She brings to those who love,
The sweet fulfillment of their secret longing.
Like a bolt out of the blue,
Fate steps in and sees you through,
When you wish upon a star your dream comes true.

© Copyright 1940 by Bourne Company, New York—Used by Permission of Bourne Music Canada Limited, Toronto, Canada (Canadian Agents).

BEAUTY AND THE BEAST

retold by Eva Martin

nce upon a time there was a young man who, when his father died, had no one left in the world. He decided that he must look for work. For three days he wandered about the country until he came at last to a village where there was a castle. He went up and knocked on the castle door.

The king himself answered. "What can I do for you, my fine fellow?" he asked.

"I am alone in the world," said the young man. "I have neither father nor mother nor sister nor brother, and I am looking for work. Do you have anything that needs to be done?"

The king thought for a moment. He looked the young man over and observed how fine and strong he was. "Yes," he said, "I could use a hard worker, as I have no sons of my own. I will adopt you and treat you like my own son. The pay will not be great, but when I die you will inherit my throne."

The young man was overjoyed at his good fortune, so he stayed at the castle, and he and the king became very fond of each other.

After several months had passed, the young prince was wandering one day through the castle grounds when he came upon a most beautiful garden. An iron fence surrounded the garden and the gate was locked. Through the fence the prince glimpsed the most rare and unusual flowers he had ever seen. He was just about to climb over the fence when a deep and fearful voice said, "Do not enter this garden or you will become an enchanted beast."

The prince looked around him but he could see no one. He climbed over the fence and gathered an armful of the beautiful flowers, for he knew that the king's birthday was near, and he wanted to give him a truly unusual gift. With the flowers in his arms, the prince was about to climb back over the fence when he saw standing before him a dreadful beast.

"You must return to this garden three times at sunset," said the beast, "and perform the task that is given you each time. Do not utter a sound, or show any fear, for if you do, you will become enchanted as I am."

The young prince, though he was very frightened, promised to return to the garden. He returned home, and when the king saw the rare and beautiful flowers that the prince presented to him, he was very much afraid.

"You have brought me a fine gift, but at what expense!" said the king, when he had heard the prince's story. "I know the garden where you found these flowers. When I was a young man, I, too, discovered that wonderful place and I was about to climb the fence when a frightful beast warned me that I would become enchanted and turn into a beast if I did so. Unlike you, I was afraid and returned home. You must keep your promise. Return at sunset and perform the task that is set for you."

At sunset, the prince once again approached the garden. The gate opened as if by magic. He entered but saw no one. Walking up the garden path, he soon came to a castle. In the castle he saw no one, but a rocking chair miraculously appeared and gently rocked as if inviting him to sit in it. The prince sat in the chair and rocked. When the clock struck nine, three dreadful giants entered the room.

"Aha," they roared. "What have we here? Is it man or beast? Who are you?" The prince said nothing. "Hmmm. The cat must have your tongue." The prince uttered not a word.

"Tell us, do you like to play games? We do, and today we feel like having a game of football, but we don't have a ball. So you will be our football." The giants picked up the prince and, using him as a football, they kicked him around with great glee until he became unconscious. Then the giants grew bored and disappeared.

The beast entered the room. She was now disenchanted to the neck, and bore the head of a beautiful young woman. Taking a small jar of ointment, she soothed the prince's wounds until he began to

regain consciousness, and then she left. The prince returned home and told the old king what had happened.

The following evening the prince returned to the garden at sunset. Once again the gate sprang open and the rocking chair was waiting for him in the castle. He sat down and at the stroke of nine, there appeared the same three horrible giants.

"Aha," they roared. "Here is the same young fellow. We didn't expect to see you again. What's your name?" The prince did not answer. "You're not going to talk to us, eh? Well, that was a good game of football we had last night. Tonight we feel like playing baseball. We've brought our bats, and since we don't have a ball, you shall be our baseball."

Although he was very much afraid, the prince said not a word. The giants picked him up and they had a great time batting him about. Finally the prince lost consciousness and the giants went away.

Once again the beast appeared. Now she was disenchanted to her waist. Taking her bottle of ointment she spread salve on the prince's wounds until he began to regain consciousness. Then she disappeared.

The prince was astonished to find himself alone and he returned home and told the king all that had happened. "Who can be helping me?" he asked.

"Perhaps you will see tonight," said the old king, "for this will be the third and final test. Go back to the beast's garden and see what awaits you."

The prince returned to the beast's castle at sunset and sat in the rocking chair once more. When the clock struck nine, the three fearsome giants entered the room.

"Aha," they cried, "tonight we shall have the most fun of all. But at least tell us your name. Perhaps we won't want to play with you after all." The prince said not a word. "Huh, I guess you've lost your voice. Perhaps we can shake it out of you."

One of the giants picked up the prince by the heels and shook him up and down, but although he trembled with fear,

the prince did not speak.

"We have just the thing for you." roared the giants. "All day long we have been digging a pit just for you. And so that you won't be bored, we have stuck sharp knives and razors into the sides of it. So here goes."

They flung the prince into the pit. By the time the prince reached the bottom, he was cut into a thousand pieces. When the prince remained silent, the giants disappeared.

What a difficult task the beast had before her. By now she was disenchanted to her legs. Gathering together all of the pieces of the prince, she joined them together with the ointment from her special bottle and at long last he opened his eyes. The prince saw standing before him the most beautiful princess that could ever be imagined. The beast was now completely disenchanted.

When the prince and princess re-entered the castle, they found a great feast awaiting them. In the middle of the celebration, an ancient fairy came into the room. She announced that the castle belonged to her and that the giants were her sons. As she had important business abroad, would the prince and princess look after the castle for her? The prince and princess were only too happy to agree.

"You may explore the castle to your heart's delight, but I forbid you to enter the room with the little green door," said the old woman.

She set off on her journey and for many days the prince and princess wandered happily through the castle, looking in all the rooms and exclaiming over the riches they found. Finally, one day, after they had seen everything there was to see, they remembered the room with the little green door.

"Surely it wouldn't hurt to take a little peek inside," they said.

On the ring of keys that the old woman had given them, they found a tiny key that fitted the little green door. When they opened the door and peeked in, they saw that the room was bare. However, when they tried to close the door, no matter how hard they pushed, it would not close.

A few days later, the old woman returned. "And how have you

been occupying your time?" she asked.

"We have explored this castle from top to bottom," they replied.

As the old woman looked about her, she saw that the little green door was open. She was very angry. "You disobeyed my orders," she said. "Therefore you will have to pay for your mistake. You will both wander for a year and a day around the shores of the Grey Sea. You will travel in that direction," she said to the prince and sent him off. "And you," she said to the princess, "will travel in the opposite direction. Here are six pairs of steel shoes. When they are worn through, you will meet your prince again. And here are three beautiful dresses—one as beautiful as the sun, one as beautiful as the moon, and one as beautiful as the stars. Take them with you."

ith tears in her heart, the princess departed on her journey. She did everything she could to wear out her steel shoes. She kicked and scuffed them against rocks and tree roots, and slid down the sides of mountains. Finally, after a year and a day, the last pair of steel shoes was worn out.

After a year and a day, the wandering prince came to a magnificent castle and hired himself out to the king. Unknowingly, the princess arrived at the same castle and obtained work looking after the sheep. As a shepherdess, she slept in a little hut in the fields close to her sheep. One morning she noticed a great flurry of activity around the castle. She asked the little boy who brought her meals what was happening. He replied that a few days earlier, a young man had come to work at the castle. The king's daughter had fallen in love with him, so the king had decided that they should marry. The princess thought to herself that perhaps this was her prince.

The next morning when she arose she put on the dress that was as beautiful as the sun. When the king's daughter looked out the window and saw a shepherd girl parading about the fields in such a beautiful dress, she called to her father, "Father, why should a mere shepherdess wear such a dress to look after the sheep? I want a dress exactly like that. After all, I am a king's daughter."

The king searched high and low through village and town but could not find a similar dress. Finally he had no choice but to go to the shepherdess and ask her to sell him the dress.

"This dress is neither for sale nor to be given away. It must be earned," the shepherdess replied.

"What do you mean?" asked the king.

"Allow me to spend the night with the young man who is going to marry your daughter and the dress is yours."

The king agreed. But before the shepherdess arrived, he filled two glasses with wine and put a sleeping potion in each one. When the young man and the shepherdess met, they each sipped some wine and fell asleep instantly.

The next morning the shepherdess returned to her hut and put on the dress that was as beautiful as the moon. When the king's

daughter saw this dress, she was filled with desire to own it as well.

The king went again to the shepherdess to ask her to give him the dress.

"Oh, no," replied the shepherdess. "This dress is not to give or sell, but must be earned. Allow me to spend a second night with the young man who is to marry your daughter. Then the dress will be yours."

The king agreed and once again he filled two glasses with wine and placed a sleeping potion in each. Unfortunately, the young man sipped the wine immediately and fell asleep. But the shepherdess threw hers away. She wrote a note to the sleeping young man, which said, "I will come again tomorrow night. Do not drink any wine, for

it is I whom you disenchanted in the beast's castle. This will be our last chance to remain together forever." She folded the paper and put it in his pocket.

The next morning, the young man discovered the note and read what the shepherdess had written.

The shepherdess returned to her hut and put on the dress that was as beautiful as the stars. The king's daughter, seeing the shepherdess's beautiful gown from her window, was furious.

"Father, how dare a shepherdess wear a dress that is fit only to be worn by a king's daughter? I must have it."

The king approached the shepherdess hoping to buy the beautiful dress.

"This dress is neither to sell nor to give, but must be earned," she replied. "Allow me to spend the night one more time with the young man who is to marry your daughter, and you shall have this beautiful dress."

For a third time, the king agreed, but this time neither the shepherdess nor the young man drank their wine. They waited until everyone was fast asleep and then they talked for a long time. They were overjoyed to discover that they were the same prince and princess who had met in the beast's garden and who had travelled around the shores of the Grey Sea before reuniting. They vowed to marry.

The next morning, the prince and princess told their story to the king. The king's daughter was so happy to own the dress that was as beautiful as the stars, that she didn't mind not marrying the young man. The king agreed to marry the prince and princess and a splendid wedding feast was arranged. People came from miles around. In the middle of the feast, a coach arrived pulled by four magnificent black horses. Inside was the ancient fairy who had sent them on their journey.

The prince and princess travelled back with the old fairy to her castle, where she said, "You have done well. You have completed your journey. Stay with me and all that I have will be yours."

A few months later the old fairy died, and the prince and princess lived happily in her castle for the rest of their lives.

from

The Crystal Child

by Barbara Wersba

The crystal statue stood in the garden, among the roses. She had once been a human child, but now she sparkled in the early sun—the folds of her dress forever neat, her eyes staring straight ahead. Her mouth was sad and perfect, like a crystal rose. Her hands were firmly clasped. As the sun climbed higher, drops of dew shone on the statue's hair. Rainbow colours washed her face, and a rabbit, hopping across the lawn, came to a halt and gazed into the statue's eyes. There was no expression there—no pain, no happiness, no fear. The statue did not seem dead and yet she was not alive either. She had simply stopped somewhere, along the road of time.

Once this child had played in the garden, had rolled a hoop along the gravelled drive that approached the house, and had sat on the large veranda drawing pictures. Once she had climbed the chestnut trees and hidden in the potting shed at the end of the lawn. That had been eighty years ago. Another family lived in the house now and no longer found it strange that a child of crystal stood among the roses. When friends asked them the origin of the statue, they could not remember. It had to do with some tragedy, they said, for the house had once burnt down. But the child had never been human. That was only a story that country people told—a myth, a piece of folklore.

Yet there were two who came to visit the child each day as though she were a friend. One was an old man who had been a gardener in the neighbourhood long ago. And the other was a boy. The gardener came to visit the statue in the morning, and the boy came after school. They had never met, but drawn by something they could not explain, each came to gaze at the crystal child—and the gardener, partly from habit, would clip away the rose stalks that brushed her dress. Standing in the early light, the man would stare at the child's old-fashioned clothes and buttoned shoes, her long hair and folded hands, and the past would come back to him like a clouded dream. To the gardener, this girl was a part of something he had lost and could not name. But unlike him, she would never grow old.

The boy was a different matter. Taking a shortcut to school one day, and crossing the lawn of the estate, he had come upon the statue and had stood transfixed. It was not just that the child was life-size and that she belonged to another era. His interest was roused by her face. The sculptured mouth was the most beautiful he had ever seen, and the eyes, though expressionless, seemed to hold depth and colour. The nose was perfect and small, and the high forehead was aristocratic. He could not take his gaze from the statue and stood there for a long time, waiting for her to speak. At last he realized how foolish this was, and went off to school. But each day he found himself returning to the garden, and each day it seemed as though the statue might speak to him. He was fourteen and the statue appeared to be a girl of twelve. Yet whenever he was with her, the boy felt that both of them were older.

The sun rose higher. Dew burned from the grass and dried on the child's crystal hair. The rainbow colours left her face and were replaced by a steady light. On a distant highway, cars and trucks could be heard. Inside the house, a telephone rang. A neighbour's dog sprinted across the lawn, barking at pigeons that clustered in the driveway. Present and past swam together in the sun while the statue glowed.

The old gardener appeared and stood staring at the girl. She looked different today, as though she had moved in the night, and her mouth was not as sad as usual. After studying her for a while, he put these thoughts away and began to clip the rose stalks that were touching her crystal dress. He had never had a child of his own and sometimes pretended that the statue was his child. Gently, he talked aloud to her. Gently, he clipped at the roses.

By late afternoon the garden was deserted. The angle of the

D. Gordon '86

sun pierced the statue like a sword, and in the western sky clouds gathered. Birds fluttered in the chestnut trees, waiting for night. The statue's eyes stared straight ahead. A starling perched on the pedestal on which she stood, and for a moment both child and bird were trapped in time. Then the boy ran across the lawn, schoolbooks under his arm, and the bird rose into the air with a cry.

Placing his books on the grass, the boy sat down cross-legged and gazed at the girl. She was becoming a part of the sunset and clouds seemed to drift through her eyes. The autumn rose petals fell about her feet. "What will happen to you when it snows?" the boy asked. "Will you feel the cold?" He thought of the statue standing in snow as the wind whipped her face. He saw a white mantle covering her dress and hair. Suddenly he longed to take her home with him, to a place where winter would not hurt her.

Hearing footsteps behind him, the boy turned and found himself staring into the eyes of the gardener. The old man had forgotten his clippers and had come back for them. For a second, neither the man nor the boy spoke. Then the gardener sat down on the grass.

"I come to visit her too," he said. "Been doing it for years."

"Why?" the boy asked.

"Don't know," said the gardener. "Don't know."

The boy felt that he did know, and that the old man had stories to tell. "I come here every day after school," he confessed. "Do you know who she is?"

The gardener gazed across the lawn. "Well, yes I do. In a way. But everyone has his own version of things. You know that."

"Who is she?"

After studying the boy, the old man seemed to change his mind about something. "It's this way," he said. "I hadn't been born yet, at the time of the fire, but when I was growing up I heard stories about it. It seems that this girl here was an only child, very sensitive and delicate, and very close to her mother. The father loved her too, but it was the mother she cared about. You understand?"

"Yes," the boy said.

"They were fine people, real gentry, and the girl had everything.

She had a governess, and a stableboy to look after her pony, and a big dollhouse that stood on the lawn. Things were different then, you see. Life was different."

"Go on."

"You won't understand."

"Yes," said the boy. "I will."

"Well . . . when the girl was around twelve years old, a fire swept the house. She escaped, and the father escaped, but the mother was killed. And it had a terrible effect on the girl. For a long time she didn't cry. Not a single tear."

"Go on," the boy said.

"Well, as I say, she didn't cry. Couldn't cry. But one day her tears came, tears for her mother, and people who were there at the time said that the tears turned into crystal. And then the child herself turned into crystal. Right before her father's eyes."

The boy showed no expression in his face. "What happened next?"

The old man sighed. "What could happen? The father took his girl and placed her here, in the garden. Then he moved away and wasn't heard of anymore. The house was rebuilt and new people moved in, and then other new people. And so it went."

"How could the father leave her?"

The gardener rose to his feet. "Don't know. But she's been here for eighty years now, and will probably be here when you and I are gone." He shook his head. "Nobody believes this story, son. Nobody at all."

Stooping slightly, the gardener walked away. And when twilight had drawn a dark veil over the sky, the boy left too. Only the statue was left behind—the crystal statue, who had heard every word they said.

from

The Phantom Tollbooth

by Norton Juster

When Milo drives his small electric car through the Phantom Tollbooth, he finds himself in The Lands Beyond. There he meets a ticking watchdog named Tock, a Humbug, and Alec, a boy who stands in mid-air. Together they travel to see a very special concert.

The sun was dropping slowly from sight, and stripes of purple and orange and crimson and gold piled themselves on top of the distant hills. The last shafts of light waited patiently for a flight of wrens to find their way home. A group of anxious stars had already taken their places.

"Here we are!" cried Alec. With a sweep of his arm, he pointed toward an enormous symphony orchestra. "Isn't it a grand sight?"

There were at least a thousand musicians ranged in a great arc before them. To the left and right were the violins and cellos, whose bows moved in great waves. Behind them in numberless profusion the piccolos, flutes, clarinets, oboes, bassoons, horns, trumpets, trombones, and tubas were all playing at once. At the very rear, so far away that they could hardly be seen were the percussion instruments. Lastly, in a long line up one side of the steep slope, were the solemn bass fiddles.

On a high podium in front stood the conductor, a tall, gaunt man with dark deep-set eyes and a thin mouth placed carelessly between his long pointed nose and his long pointed chin. He used no baton, but conducted with large, sweeping movements which seemed to start at his toes and work slowly up through his body and along his slender arms and end finally at the tips of his graceful fingers.

"I don't hear any music," said Milo.

"That's right," said Alec; "you don't listen to this concert—you watch it. Now, pay attention."

As the conductor waved his arms, he moulded the air like handfuls of soft clay. The musicians carefully followed his every direction.

"What are they playing?" asked Tock, looking up inquisitively at Alec.

"The sunset, of course. They play it every evening, about this time."

"They do?" said Milo quizzically.

"Naturally," answered Alec, "and they also play morning, noon, and night, when, of course, it's morning, noon, or night. Why, there wouldn't be any colour in the world unless they played it. Each instrument plays a different one," he explained. "And depending on what season it is and how the weather's to be, the conductor chooses his score and directs the day. But watch: the sun has almost set, and in a moment you can ask Chroma himself."

The last colours slowly faded from the western sky, and as they did, one by one the instruments stopped until only the bass fiddles, in their somber slow movements, were left to play the night and a single set of silver bells to brighten the constellations. The conductor let his arms fall limply at his sides and stood quite still as darkness claimed the forest.

"That was a very beautiful sunset," said Milo, walking to the podium.

"It should be," was the reply; "we've been practising since the world began." And reaching down, the speaker picked Milo off the ground and set him on the music stand. "I am Chroma the Great," he continued, gesturing broadly with his hands, "conductor of colour, maestro of pigment, and director of the entire spectrum."

"Do you play all day long?" asked Milo when he had introduced himself.

"Ah yes, all day, every day," he sang out, then pirouetted gracefully around the platform. "I rest only at night, and even then *they* play on."

"What would happen if you stopped?" asked Milo. He didn't quite believe that colour happened that way.

"See for yourself," roared Chroma, and he raised both hands high over his head. Immediately the instruments that were playing stopped. At once all colour vanished. The world looked like an enormous colouring book that had never been used. Everything appeared in simple black outlines as if someone with a set of paints the size of a house and a brush as wide could stay happily occupied for years. Then Chroma lowered his arms. The instruments began again and the colour returned.

"You see what a dull place the world would be without colour?" he said, bowing until his chin almost touched the ground. "But what pleasure to lead my violins in a serenade of spring green or hear my trumpets blare out the blue sea and then watch the oboes tint it all

in warm yellow sunshine. Rainbows are best of all—and blazing neon signs, and taxicabs with stripes, and the soft, muted tones of a foggy day. We play them all."

As Chroma spoke, Milo sat with his eyes open wide, and Alec, Tock, and the Humbug looked on in wonder.

"Now I really must get some sleep." Chroma yawned. "We've had lightning, fireworks, and parades for the last few nights, and I've had to be up to conduct them. But tonight is sure to be quiet." Then, putting his large hand on Milo's shoulder, he said, "Be a good fellow and watch my orchestra till morning, will you? And be sure to wake me at 5:23 for the sunrise. Good night, good night, good night."

With that he leaped lightly from the podium and, in three long steps, vanished into the forest.

"That's a good idea," said Tock, making himself comfortable in the grass as the bug grumbled himself quickly to sleep and Alec stretched out in mid-air.

And Milo, full of thoughts and questions, curled up on the pages of tomorrow's music and eagerly awaited the dawn.

One by one, the hours passed and at exactly 5:22 (by Tock's very accurate clock) Milo carefully opened one eye, and, in a moment, the other. Everything was still purple, dark blue, and black, yet scarcely a minute remained to the long, quiet night.

He stretched lazily, rubbed his eyelids, scratched his head, and shivered once as a greeting to the early-morning mist.

"I must wake Chroma for the sunrise," he said softly. Then he suddenly wondered what it would be like to lead the orchestra and to colour the whole world himself.

The idea whirled through his thoughts. He quickly decided that it couldn't be very difficult, since the musicians probably all knew what to do by themselves anyway. It did seem a shame to wake anyone so early, and it might be his only chance. The musicians were already poised and ready. He would try—but just for a little while.

And so, as everyone slept peacefully on, Milo stood on tiptoes, raised his arms slowly in front of him, and made the slightest movement possible with the index finger of his right hand. It was now 5:23 a.m.

As if understanding his signal perfectly, a single piccolo played a single note and off in the east, a solitary shaft of cool lemon light flicked across the sky. Milo smiled happily and then cautiously crooked his finger again. This time two more piccolos and a flute joined in and three more rays of light danced into view. Then with both hands he made a great circular sweep in the air and watched with delight as all the musicians began to play at once.

The cellos made the hills glow red. The leaves and grass were tipped with a soft pale green as the violins began their song. Only the bass fiddles rested as the entire orchestra washed the forest in colour.

Milo was overjoyed because they were all playing for him, and just the way they should.

"Won't Chroma be surprised?" he thought, signalling the musicians to stop. "I'll wake him now."

But, instead of stopping, they continued to play even louder than before until each colour became more brilliant than he thought possible. Milo shielded his eyes with one hand and waved the other desperately, but the colours continued to grow brighter and brighter and brighter. Then an even more curious thing began to happen.

As Milo frantically conducted, the sky changed slowly from blue to tan and then to a rich magenta red. Flurries of light-green snow began to fall. The leaves on the trees and bushes turned a vivid orange. All the flowers suddenly appeared black, the grey rocks became a lovely soft chartreuse, and even peacefully sleeping Tock changed from brown to a magnificent ultramarine. Nothing was the colour it should have been. Yet the more Milo tried to straighten things out, the worse they became.

"I wish I hadn't started," he thought unhappily as a pale-blue blackbird flew by. "There doesn't seem to be any way to stop them."

He tried very hard to do everything just the way Chroma had done, but nothing worked. The musicians played on, faster and faster, and the purple sun raced quickly across the sky. In less than a minute it had set once more in the west and then, without any pause, risen again in the east. The sky was now quite yellow and the grass a charming shade of lavender. Seven times the sun rose and almost as quickly disappeared as the colours kept changing. In just a few minutes a whole week had gone by.

At last the exhausted Milo, afraid to call for help and on the verge of tears, dropped his hands to his sides. The orchestra stopped. The colours disappeared, and once again it was night. The time was 5:27 a.m.

"Wake up, everybody! Time for the sunrise!" he shouted with relief, and quickly jumped from the music stand.

"What a marvellous rest," said Chroma, striding to the podium. "I feel as though I'd slept for a week. My, my, I see we're a little late this morning. I'll have to cut my lunch hour short by four minutes."

He tapped for attention, and this time the dawn proceeded perfectly. "You did a fine job," he said, patting Milo on the head. "Someday I'll let you conduct the orchestra yourself."

Tock wagged his tail proudly, but Milo didn't say a word. To this day no one knows of the lost week but the few people who happened to be awake at 5:23 on that very strange morning.

from

THE LION, THE WITCH AND THE WARDROBE

by C. S. Lewis

On a rainy day Lucy and her brothers and sister decide to explore the huge, mysterious mansion of an old Professor who has invited them to visit. They come across a room completely empty except for one big wardrobe. The others move on, but Lucy is curious. She steps into the wardrobe, edges her way further and further in through long fur coats and suddenly finds herself in a land of snow and pine forests. There she bumps into a Faun.

"Good evening," said Lucy. But the Faun was so busy picking up its parcels that at first it did not reply. When it had finished it made her a little bow.

"Good evening, good evening," said the Faun. "Excuse me—I don't want to be inquisitive—but should I be right in thinking that you are a Daughter of Eve?"

"My name's Lucy," said she, not quite understanding him.

"But you are—forgive me—you are what they call a girl?" asked the Faun.

"Of course I'm a girl," said Lucy.

"You are in fact Human?"

"Of course I'm human," said Lucy, still a little puzzled.

"To be sure, to be sure," said the Faun. "How stupid of me! But I've never seen a Son of Adam or a Daughter of Eve before. I am delighted. That is to say—" and then it stopped as if it had been going to say something it had not intended but had remembered in time. "Delighted, delighted," it went on. "Allow me to introduce myself. My name is Tumnus."

"I am very pleased to meet you, Mr. Tumnus," said Lucy.

"And may I ask, O Lucy Daughter of Eve," said Mr. Tumnus, "how you have come into Narnia?"

"Narnia? What's that?" said Lucy.

"This is the land of Narnia," said the Faun, "where we are now; all that lies between the lamp-post and the great castle of Cair Paravel on the eastern sea. And you—you have come from the wild woods of the west?"

"I—I got in through the wardrobe in the spare room," said Lucy.

"Ah!" said Mr. Tumnus in a rather melancholy voice, "if only I had worked harder at geography when I was a little Faun, I should no doubt know all about those strange countries. It is too late now."

"But they aren't countries at all," said Lucy, almost laughing. "It's only just back there—at least—I'm not sure. It is summer there."

"Meanwhile," said Mr. Tumnus, "it is winter in Narnia, and has been for ever so long, and we shall both catch cold if we stand here talking in the snow. Daughter of Eve from the far land of Spare Oom where eternal summer reigns around the bright city of War Drobe, how would it be if you came and had tea with me?"

"Thank you very much, Mr. Tumnus," said Lucy. "But I was wondering whether I ought to be getting back."

"It's only just round the corner," said the Faun, "and there'll be a roaring fire—and toast—and sardines—and cake."

"Well, it's very kind of you," said Lucy. "But I shan't be able to stay long."

"If you will take my arm, Daughter of Eve," said Mr. Tumnus,

"I shall be able to hold the umbrella over both of us. That's the way. Now—off we go."

And so Lucy found herself walking through the wood arm in arm with this strange creature as if they had known one another all their lives.

They had not gone far before they came to a place where the ground became rough and there were rocks all about and little hills up and little hills down. At the bottom of one small valley Mr. Tumnus turned suddenly aside as if he were going to walk straight into an unusually large rock, but at the last moment Lucy found he was leading her into the entrance of a cave. As soon as they were inside she found herself blinking in the light of a wood fire. Then Mr. Tumnus stooped and took a flaming piece of wood out of the fire with a neat little pair of tongs, and lit a lamp. "Now we shan't be long," he said, and immediately put a kettle on.

Lucy thought she had never been in a nicer place. It was a little, dry, clean cave of reddish stone with a carpet on the floor and two little chairs ("one for me and one for a friend," said Mr. Tumnus) and a table and a dresser and a mantelpiece over the fire and above that a picture of an old Faun with a grey beard. In one corner there was a door which Lucy thought must lead to Mr. Tumnus's bedroom, and on one wall was a shelf full of books. Lucy looked at these while he was setting out the tea things. They had titles like *The Life and Letters of Silenus* or *Nymphs and Their Ways* or *Men, Monks and Gamekeepers; a Study in Popular Legend* or *Is Man a Myth?*

"Now, Daughter of Eve!" said the Faun.

And really it was a wonderful tea. There was a nice brown egg, lightly boiled, for each of them, and then sardines on toast, and then buttered toast, and then toast with honey, and then a sugar-topped cake. And when Lucy was tired of eating the Faun began to talk. He had wonderful tales to tell of life in the forest. He told about the midnight dances and how the Nymphs who lived in the wells and the Dryads who lived in the trees came out to dance with the Fauns; about long hunting parties after the milk-white stag who could give you wishes if you caught him; about feasting and treasure-seeking with the wild Red Dwarfs in deep mines and caverns far beneath the forest floor; and then about summer when the woods were green and old Silenus on his fat donkey would come to visit them, and sometimes Bacchus himself, and then the streams would run with wine instead of water and the whole forest would give itself up to jollification for weeks on end. "Not that it isn't always winter now," he added gloomily. Then to cheer himself up he took out from its case on the dresser a strange little flute that looked as if it were made of straw and began to play. And the tune he played made Lucy

want to cry and laugh and dance and go to sleep all at the same time. It must have been hours later when she shook herself and said:

"Oh, Mr. Tumnus—I'm so sorry to stop you, and I do love that tune—but really, I must go home. I only meant to stay for a few minutes."

"It's no good *now*, you know," said the Faun, laying down its flute and shaking its head at her very sorrowfully.

"No good?" said Lucy, jumping up and feeling rather frightened. "What do you mean? I've got to go home at once. The others will be

wondering what has happened to me." But a moment later she asked, "Mr. Tumnus! Whatever is the matter?" for the Faun's brown eyes had filled with tears and then the tears began trickling down its cheeks, and soon they were running off the end of its nose; and at last it covered its face with its hands and began to howl.

"Mr. Tumnus! Mr. Tumnus!" said Lucy in great distress. "Don't! Don't! What is the matter? Aren't you well? Dear Mr. Tumnus, do tell me what is wrong." But the Faun continued sobbing as if its heart would break. And even when Lucy went over and put her arms round him and lent him her handkerchief, he did not stop. He merely took the handkerchief and kept on using it, wringing it out with both hands whenever it got too wet to be anymore use, so that presently Lucy was standing in a damp patch.

"Mr. Tumnus!" bawled Lucy in his ear, shaking him. "Do stop. Stop it at once! You ought to be ashamed of yourself, a great big Faun like you. What on earth are you crying about?"

"Oh–oh–oh!" sobbed Mr. Tumnus, "I'm crying because I'm such a bad Faun."

"I don't think you're a bad Faun at all," said Lucy. "I think you are a very good Faun. You are the nicest Faun I've ever met."

"Oh–oh–you wouldn't say that if you knew," replied Mr. Tumnus between his sobs. "No, I'm a bad Faun. I don't suppose there ever was a worse Faun since the beginning of the world."

"But what have you done?" asked Lucy.

"My old father, now," said Mr. Tumnus; "that's his picture over the mantelpiece. He would never have done a thing like this."

"A thing like what?" said Lucy.

"Like what I've done," said the Faun. "Taken service under the White Witch. That's what I am. I'm in the pay of the White Witch."

"The White Witch? Who is she?"

"Why, it is she that has got all Narnia under her thumb. It's she that makes it always winter. Always winter and never Christmas; think of that!"

"How awful!" said Lucy. "But what does she pay you for?"

"That's the worst of it," said Mr. Tumnus with a deep groan.

"I'm a kidnapper for her, that's what I am. Look at me, Daughter of Eve. Would you believe that I'm the sort of Faun to meet a poor innocent child in the wood, one that had never done me any harm, and pretend to be friendly with it, and invite it home to my cave, all for the sake of lulling it asleep and then handing it over to the White Witch?"

"No," said Lucy. "I'm sure you wouldn't do anything of the sort."

"But I have," said the Faun.

"Well," said Lucy rather slowly (for she wanted to be truthful and yet not be too hard on him), "well, that was pretty bad. But you're so sorry for it that I'm sure you will never do it again."

"Daughter of Eve, don't you understand?" said the Faun. "It isn't something I *have* done. I'm doing it now, this very moment."

"What do you mean?" cried Lucy, turning very white.

"You are the child," said Tumnus. "I had orders from the White Witch that if ever I saw a Son of Adam or a Daughter of Eve in the wood, I was to catch them and hand them over to her. And you are the first I ever met. And I've pretended to be your friend and asked you to tea, and all the time I've been meaning to wait till you were asleep and then go and tell *Her*."

"Oh, but you won't, Mr. Tumnus," said Lucy. "You won't, will you? Indeed, indeed you really mustn't."

"And if I don't," said he, beginning to cry again, "she's sure to find out. And she'll have my tail cut off, and my horns sawn off, and my beard plucked out, and she'll wave her wand over my beautiful cloven hoofs and turn them into horrid solid hoofs like a wretched horse's. And if she is extra and specially angry she'll turn me into stone and I shall be only a statue of a Faun in her horrible house until the four thrones at Cair Paravel are filled—and goodness knows when that will happen, or whether it will ever happen at all."

"I'm very sorry, Mr. Tumnus," said Lucy. "But please let me go home."

"Of course I will," said the Faun. "Of course I've got to. I see that now. I hadn't known what Humans were like before I met you. Of course I can't give you up to the Witch; not now that I know you.

But we must be off at once. I'll send you back to the lamp-post. I suppose you can find your own way from there back to Spare Oom and War Drobe?"

"I'm sure I can," said Lucy.

"We must go as quietly as we can," said Mr. Tumnus. "The whole wood is full of *her* spies. Even some of the trees are on her side."

They both got up and left the tea things on the table, and Mr. Tumnus once more put up his umbrella and gave Lucy his arm, and they went out into the snow. The journey back was not at all like the journey to the Faun's cave; they stole along as quickly as they could, without speaking a word, and Mr. Tumnus kept to the darkest places. Lucy was relieved when they reached the lamp-post again.

"Do you know your way from here, Daughter of Eve?" said Tumnus.

Lucy looked very hard between the trees and could just see in the distance a patch of light that looked like daylight. "Yes," she said, "I can see the wardrobe door."

"Then be off home as quick as you can," said the Faun, "and—c-can you ever forgive me for what I meant to do?"

"Why, of course I can," said Lucy, shaking him heartily by the hand. "And I do hope you won't get into dreadful trouble on my account."

"Farewell, Daughter of Eve," said he. "Perhaps I may keep the handkerchief?"

"Rather!" said Lucy, and then ran towards the far-off patch of daylight as quickly as her legs would carry her. And presently instead of rough branches brushing past her she felt coats, and instead of crunching snow under her feet she felt wooden boards, and all at once she found herself jumping out of the wardrobe into the same empty room from which the whole adventure had started. She shut the wardrobe door tightly behind her and looked around, panting for breath. It was still raining and she could hear the voices of the others in the passage.

"I'm here," she shouted. "I'm here. I've come back, I'm all right."

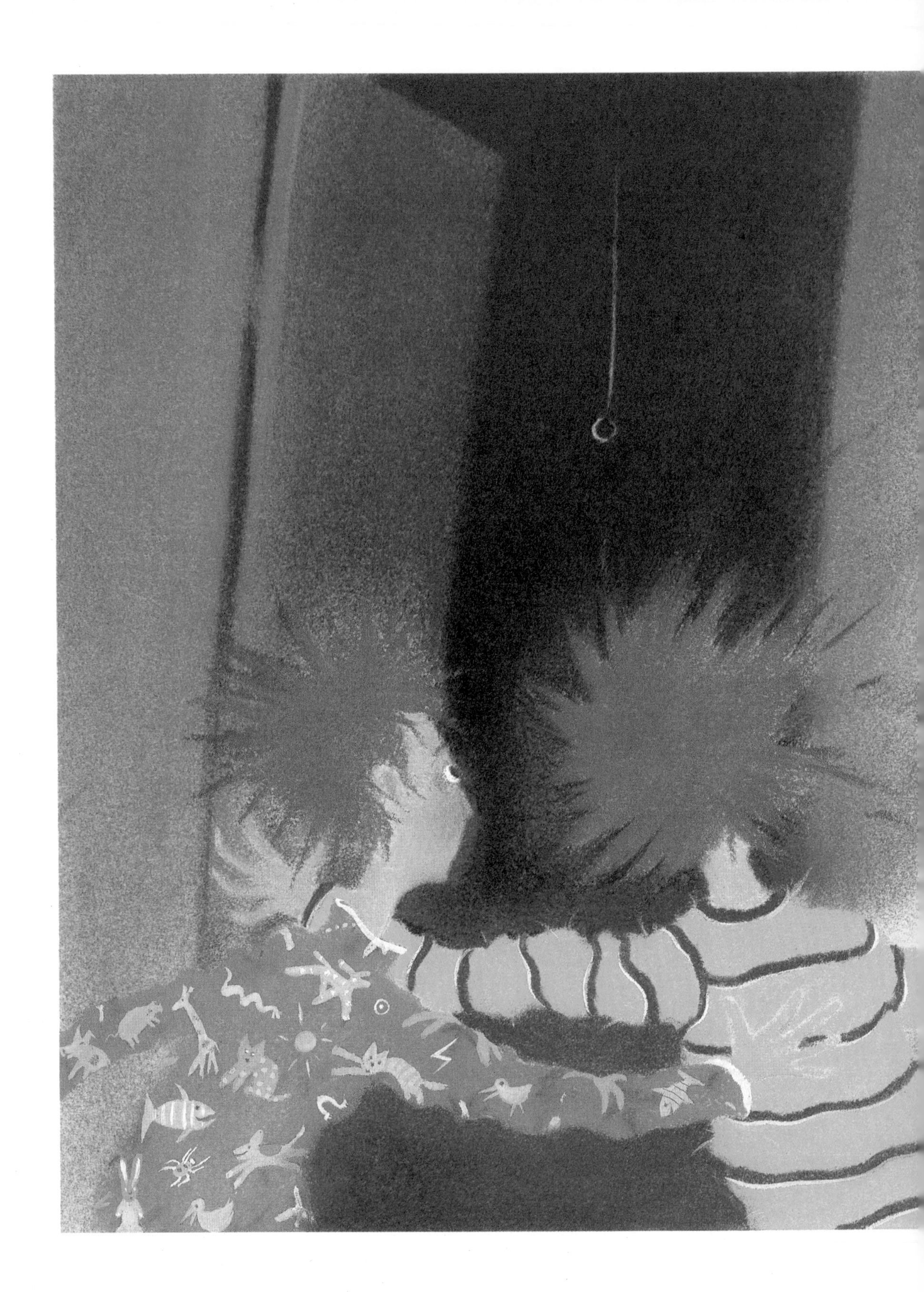

Pushed

by Diane Dawber

"You go first!"

"No. You go first."

Neither one of us
wants to go
first into the dark room
with the light switch
on a string
a few steps beyond.

"You go first."

"No. You."

Though my hands are
clutching the door frame
my sister
pushes me in and slams the door.

She didn't have
to slam the door.

Lost His Marbles

by Diane Dawber

I had marbles
blue and red from the Chinese checkers
and clear ones with stripes
from the tea bag packages.

On the way to school
Pete asked if I wanted to play
so we set one in the centre
and tried to hit it.

I did
over and over
won
all his marbles.

Now they
won't let me play anymore.

from

NED KELLY AND THE CITY OF THE BEES

by Thomas Keneally

As Ned Kelly lies in a hospital bed, he watches a bee fly from the windowsill to land on his chest. The bee crawls up to his chin and offers him a drop of golden liquid. As soon as he drinks it, he shrinks to the size of a bee himself. And so he meets Apis, a worker bee, and Nancy Clancy, who speaks in rhymes and is a hundred and twenty years old. They take him to their beehive to meet the Queen.

"It's morning," said Nancy Clancy, shaking my elbow. "I've been up half an hour practising my rhymes."

"Oh," I said. I sat up, dangling my legs over the end of Miss Nancy Clancy's bed. I still wasn't certain where I was, and my head felt put on crooked, as your head often does when you first wake up.

"Cheer up," she told me. "You'll probably see the Queen today." Then she frowned. She had thought of something that had nothing to do with beehives and early morning. "I wonder why people say cheer up instead of cheer down. Consider this, if you're not cheerful you're upset and if you're *up*set then you should cheer *down*. Don't you think?"

"If you like," I sighed. I wasn't in the mood for arguing. I was missing my mother and father.

"All right," Miss Nancy Clancy decided. "From now on we both cheer down." Before I had any chance to cheer down, two bees appeared at the doorway of the apartment. One carried a bead of royal jelly, the other a drop of water which looked like a jewel in the hive's dim light. Nancy Clancy ran to collect both the jelly and the water in cups. She handed both cups to me and I began to eat the jelly and drink the water, but slowly.

"Come on, eat up!" she said. "Though that's another ridiculous phrase of course. How can you eat *up* when the food travels down from your mouth to your stomach?" I was feeling better now and so I began to discuss the question with her.

"You pick it *up* from the plate or the cup to eat it," I explained.

"Well in that case you can pick up but eat down. That's what we'll say from now on."

"You can say it. I won't."

"All right," she said, sniffing and turning her face away. "If you want to be as stupid as all other humans, you go ahead eating up. I'll eat down and I'll cheer down, and when you're a hundred and twenty years like me, you'll see I was right."

At this point of the argument Apis poked her head round the edge of the cell.

"Good morning," she said in her husky voice.

"*Good morning to you, faithful bee*," Nancy Clancy replied,

"*And what have you got to show to we?*"

"Well, if you both hurry we can see the Queen go by."

Nancy Clancy rushed me to the cell door and we looked down. Below us a beautiful bee, much bigger than Apis, much longer than Romeo the drone, was swaying slowly across the wall of honeycomb. Other bees, workers and servants, guards and fanning bees to keep

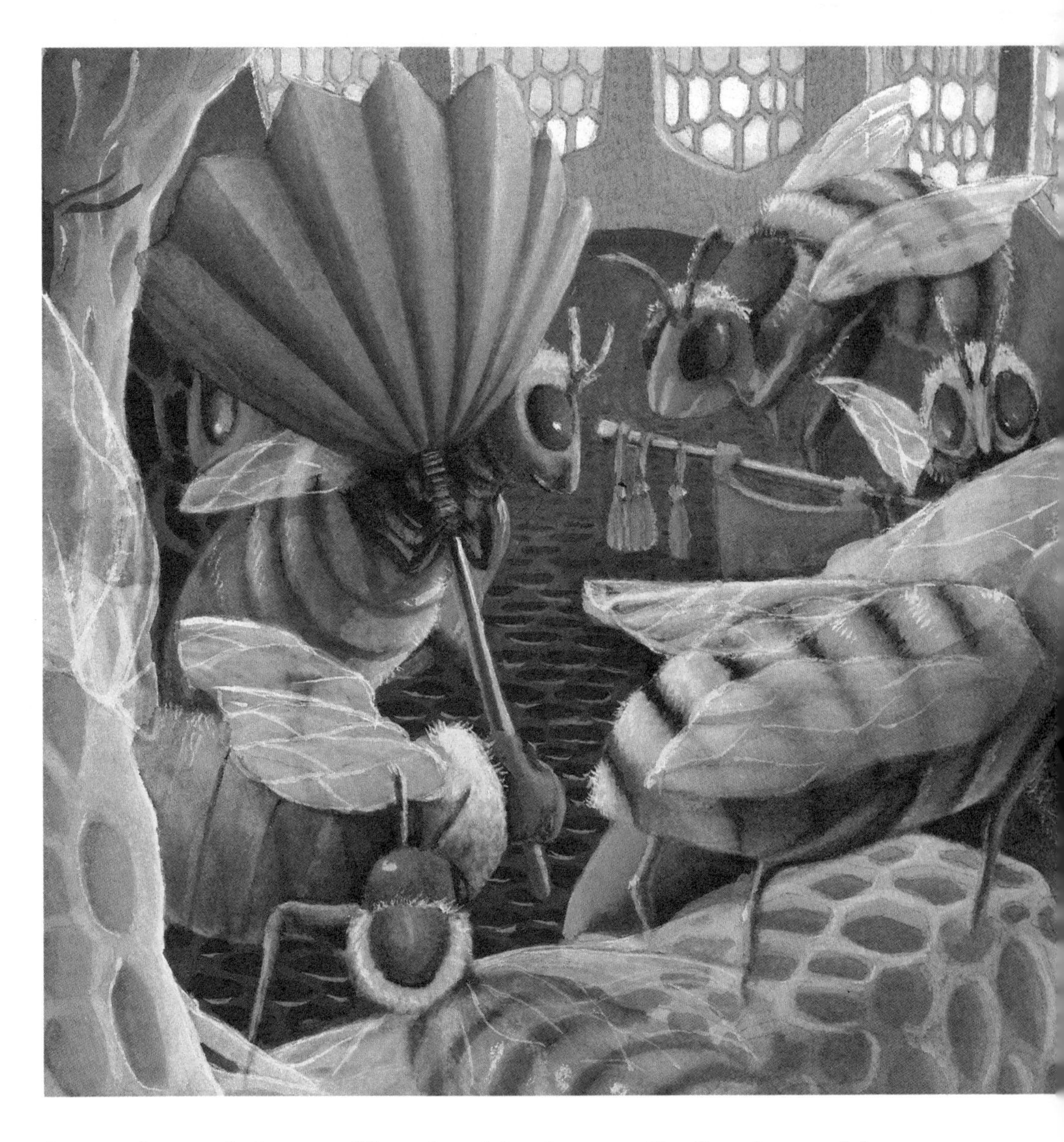

her cool, crowded around her, touching her gently, fanning and fussing. She walked more gracefully than a racehorse or any other animal I had ever seen. Her waist was thinner than the waist on the models in the front window of Murphy's dress shop, and her wings, which were no bigger than Apis's wings, were folded over her back.

She's on her way to lay eggs," Apis explained. "But she might have a moment to meet you."

Apis left us, climbed down the wall, dragged two young fanning bees away from the Queen by their hind legs, and rushed into the empty space at the Queen's side. We could see the Queen and Apis

talking, touching each other gently with their feelers. Then Apis turned away and led the Queen up the wall towards us.

I felt nervous and started combing my hair with my fingers. When Apis was close to us again she whispered, "If you talk in rhymes, Miss Clancy, I promise I'll sting you."

At last the Queen stood at the door, her feelers swaying gracefully and her beautiful molten eyes looking at us. Apis coughed. "Her Majesty decided to come and visit you only because you aren't good at climbing up and down the honeycomb."

"I'm all right at it," Nancy Clancy muttered. She pointed to me.

"But my friend isn't yet accustomed to it."

Apis coughed again. "This, your Majesty, is Miss Nancy Clancy whom you already know, and this is Ned. Ned and Nancy, Queen Selma."

"What would you like me to say, you two?" Queen Selma asked in a slightly cracked voice.

I was surprised to find she could talk just the same as Apis, and my mouth must have hung open for a second. The Queen noticed it, laughed, and began talking fast.

"Oh yes," she said, "my good friend Apis has taught me how to talk radio. I can say, *Good morning, children* like Mrs. Martin in *Martin's Corner* or I can say *G'day, kids* like Dave in *Dad and Dave.* Which would you prefer to hear?"

I was speechless as Selma rattled off the names of radio shows, but Miss Nancy Clancy was able to say, "I think I'd like to hear *Good morning, children.*"

"All right," said the Queen. "*Good morning, children!*"

"Good morning, Your Majesty," Nancy Clancy sang, bowing as low as she could on the crooked floor.

"Now," said Queen Selma, looking at me with large black eyes, "I have to ask this young man some questions, grill him, get him to come clean. Miss Nancy Clancy tells me that when she was young there was a queen called Victoria who never laid any eggs. Is she still alive?"

"No," I said. "No, Queen Victoria died a long time ago."

"Of course," Selma sniffed. "No one wants a queen who doesn't lay eggs."

I thought it wouldn't be polite to tell the beautiful Selma that humans never expected Queen Victoria to lay eggs.

"Enjoy your stay then," said Queen Selma. "And, as they say in *Rick the Frontier Scout, I'm gonna head down that there canyon.* Good morning."

She waved her feelers especially gracefully, turned and swayed away, and all the fanners and escort bees fell in at her side, marching sideways, keeping her company.

The Stars in the Sky

retold by Ethel Johnston Phelps

There once was a girl who wanted to touch the stars in the sky. On clear nights, when she looked through her bedroom window, the stars twinkled and glittered in the velvet blackness of the sky above. Sometimes the stars seemed like diamonds, sometimes like tears, and sometimes like merry eyes.

One summer evening the lass set off to seek the stars. She walked and walked until she came to the dark, satiny surface of a millpond.

"Good evening," said she. "I'm seeking the stars in the sky. Can you help me?"

"They're right here," murmured the pond. "They shine so brightly on my face that I can't sleep nights. Jump in, lass. See if you can catch one."

The lass jumped into the pond and swam all around it. But never a star did she find.

She walked on across the fields until she came to a chattering brook.

"Good evening," said she. "I'm off to find the stars in the sky. Do you know how to reach them?"

"Yes, yes. They're always dancing about on the stones and water here," chattered the brook. "Come in and catch one if you can."

The lass waded in, but not a star could she find in the brook.

"I don't think the stars come down here at all!" she cried.

"Well, they *look* as if they're here," said the brook pertly. "And isn't that the same thing?"

"Not the same thing at all," said the girl.

She walked on until she met a host of Little Folk dancing on the grass. No taller than herself, they seemed very elegant in their clothes of green and gold.

"Good evening to you, Little Folk of the Hill," she called, taking care to be polite. "I'm seeking the stars in the sky."

High, silvery voices rang out. "They shine on the grass here at night. Come dance with us if you want to find one."

The lass joined the round ring dance of the Little Folk and danced and danced. But although the grass twinkled and gleamed beneath their feet, not a star did she find.

She left the dancers and sat down beyond the ring, "I've searched and searched, but there are no stars down here," she cried. "Can't you tell me how to reach the stars?"

The dancers simply laughed. Then one of the company came over to her and said, "Since you're so set on it, I'll give you this advice. If you won't go back, go forward. Keep going forward; and mind you take the right road. Ask Four-Feet to carry you to No-Feet-At-All. Then tell No-Feet-At-All to carry you to the Stairs Without Steps. If you can climb them—"

"If I can, will I be up among the stars in the sky at last?" she asked.

"If you're not there, you'll be somewhere else," said the Little Man, and he ran back to join the dancers.

With a light heart, the lass stood up and went forward. Just as she was beginning to doubt that she was on the right road, she came to a silver-grey horse beneath a rowan tree.

"Good evening," said the lass. "I'm seeking the stars in the sky and my feet are weary. Will you carry me along the way?"

"I know nothing about stars in the sky," said the horse. "I am here to do the bidding of the Little Folk only."

"I've just been dancing with them, and I was told to ask Four-Feet to carry me to No-Feet-At-All."

"In that case, climb on my back," said the horse. "I am Four-Feet, and I will take you there."

They rode on and on until they left the woods behind and came to the edge of the land. Before them on the water, a wide, gleaming path of silver ran straight out to sea. And in the distance, a wonderful arch of brilliant colours rose from the water and went right up into the sky.

"I've brought you to the end of land," said the horse. "That's as much as Four-Feet can do for you. Climb down now; I must be off."

The lass slid from the horse and stood on the shore, looking about her. A large fish swam in from the sea.

"Good evening, fish," she called. "I'm looking for the stars in the sky. Can you show me the way?"

"Not unless you bring the word of the Little Folk," said the fish.

"I can indeed," she answered. "Four-Feet brought me here, and I was told No-Feet-At-All would carry me to the Stairs Without Steps."

"In that case," said the fish, "I will take you. Sit on my back and hold tight."

Off he swam with the girl on his back, straight along the silver path toward the bright arch of many colours. As they came to the foot of it, she saw the broad stairs of colour rising steeply into the sky. At the far end of it were the merry, glittering stars.

"Here you are," said the fish. "These are the Stairs Without Steps. They're not easy to climb. Climb if you can, but mind you hold fast and don't fall!"

So she started off. It was not easy at all to climb the bright-coloured light. She climbed on and on, and it seemed she moved very slowly. Although she was high above the sea, the stars were still far away.

She was very weary but she thought, "I've come this far. I won't give up now."

On and on she went. The air grew colder, the light more brilliant, until at last she reached the top of the arch. All about her the stars darted, raced, and spun in dazzling flashes of light. Below her, stretching down into darkness, were the brilliant colours of the Stairs Without Steps.

She had reached the stars in the sky at last, and she stood transfixed with joy at the sheer wonder of it all.

After a time she became aware that the air was icy cold, and the hard, brilliant light of the spinning stars made her dizzy. Shading her eyes with her hand, she tried to see the earth below, but all was in darkness. No warm flicker of hearth or candlelight could be seen.

Then, in one last yearning effort, she stretched out her hand to touch a flashing star. She reached farther, farther—until suddenly

she lost her balance. With a sigh—half of regret, half of contentment—she slid down, down, faster and faster into the darkness below, and all sense left her.

When she opened her eyes it was morning. The sun shone warm and golden on her bed.

"I *did* reach the stars!" she thought with joy. But in the safe stillness of her room she wondered, "Or did I dream it?"

Then she opened her tightly curled right hand, and on her palm lay a brilliant speck of stardust.

The Long-Haired Boy

by Shel Silverstein

There was a boy in our town with long hair—
I mean really long hair—
And everybody pointed at him
And laughed at him
And made fun of him.
And when he walked down the street
The people would roar
And stick their tongues out
And make funny faces
And run in and slam their door
And shout at him from the window
Until he couldn't stand it anymore.
So he sat down and cried
Till his whole body shook,
And pretty soon his hair shook too,
And it flapped
And flapped—
And he lifted—
And flew—

Straight up in the air like a helicopter.
Jenny Ricks saw him and dropped her
Knitting and screamed, "It's a flying kid!"
Lukey Hastings ran and hid
Under Old Man Merrill's car,
Miss Terance fainted, Henry Quist
Tried to shoot him down, but missed—
"I thought he was a crow," he said.
And 'round he sailed all through the day,
Smiling in the strangest way,
With the wind in his hair
And the sun in his eyes.
We saw him swoop and bank and rise.
He brushed the treetops
And skimmed the grass
On Yerbey's lawn and almost crashed
Right into Hansen's silo—but
Zoomed up in time and almost hit
The courthouse. Old Man Cooley bit
Right through his napkin when he saw
A kid fly through the diner door—
And out of the window, tipping the ladder—

Where Smokey was painting, he almost had a
Heart attack—he clung to a rafter.
The kid flew on—
Us runnin' after,
Cheering and sweating
And screaming, "Hooray!"
Mayor Lowry shouted, "Hey—
Come down here, kid. We'd like to say
How proud of you we are today.
Who ever thought our little
Town would have a hero in it?
So I'd like to proclaim this day—hey, kid!
Will you please come down for just a minute?"
But the flying kid did not come down.
He treaded air above the town,
Sort of cryin' and looking down
At all of us here on the ground.
Then up he flew, up into the clouds,
Flapping and flying so far and high,
Out past the hills and into the sky
Until a tiny speck against the sun
Was all we could see of him . . . then he was gone.

Tongue Twisters

Ten thatchers went to thatch
ten tin thatched cottages,
taking ten tight bundles of thatching straw
with them to thatch with.

Tom threw Tim three thumbtacks.

If a woodchuck could chuck wood,
how much wood would a woodchuck chuck
if a woodchuck could chuck wood?
He would chuck, he would,
as much as he could,
if a woodchuck could chuck wood.

A tree toad loved a she-toad
That lived up in a tree.
She was a three-toed tree toad,
But a two-toed toad was he.
The two-toed toad tried to win
The she-toad's friendly nod,
For the two-toed toad loved the ground
On which the three-toed toad trod,
But no matter how the two-toed tree toad tried,
He could not please her whim.
In her tree-toad bower,
With her three-toed power,
The she-toad vetoed him.

A white witch watched a
woebegone walrus
winding white wool.

Esau Wood sawed wood. One day Esau Wood saw a saw saw wood. Of all the woodsaws Wood ever saw saw wood, Wood never saw a woodsaw that would saw wood like the woodsaw Wood saw would saw wood. Now Esau Wood saws with that saw he saw saw wood.

In the Way

Have you ever felt that you were in the way, and that others did not seem to care about your feelings? Even in the happiest of families or in the best of friendships, there may be times when a relationship runs into trouble. Sometimes reading about other characters in similar situations can help you to recognize the difficulties you have that arise from being close to others. In this excerpt, Brigitte feels alone and confused.

She stopped at a fish stand. She saw a basket filled with strange objects that looked like chestnut burrs. She fingered them to see if they felt as prickly as they looked. The man who was slicing a slippery fish with a long sharp knife frowned at her.

"Don't handle the seafood, little one," he said, "unless your mother has sent you to buy some."

Brigitte quickly moved away. She pushed her way through the shoppers and stopped in front of a farm woman's stall.

"Don't stand in front of my cabbages, little girl," said the farm woman. "What housewife will buy cabbages that she cannot see?"

So Brigitte slowly walked away until she came to a man who was selling aprons. He stopped her as she went by.

"A nice apron for your mama?" he wheedled. Then he put an apron on himself and tied it round the back to show her how nice her mama would look in it.

"I have no mama," said Brigitte. "I—I mean I have many mamas." Then because she knew her explanation sounded silly, she blushed and darted away. She went to the pavement where the market lorries were parked and looked fearfully across the street to the houses where the wicked dogs lived.

Then a woman with a scarf over her head bumped her four-wheeled market cart into Brigitte's knees. "Why aren't you in school instead of in the way?" chided the woman.

(from *The Happy Orpheline* by Natalie Savage Carlson)

What do you think Brigitte meant when she said, "I have many mamas"? In looking at relationships inside stories, we will see all types of families and friendships, and you may recognize your own viewpoint and perhaps some of your own feelings as you read. In this section, you will meet some people who felt "in the way," and who found out that it is possible to build better and stronger relationships.

8734
X 43

from

Nothing's Fair in Fifth Grade

by Barthe DeClements

The morning of the day report cards came out, Mrs. Hanson called each of us to her desk. She wanted us to look at the report card and discuss it with her if we didn't think it was fair. If some kid complained, Mrs. Hanson wrote down all his scores and asked him to average them. No one objected to a grade unless it was a real mistake. Nobody wanted to do all that math for nothing.

When I got called up to her desk, I was scared but still hoping for a miracle. I didn't get a miracle. I got a D minus. Two As, three Bs, and a lousy D minus. Diane wrote a note asking me what I got.

Elsie was the next one called up. I didn't really see what happened. I was too busy writing a note back to Diane, telling her I was going to get killed when I got home. What jerked me out of my note writing were the yells and laughter and Mrs. Hanson saying over and over, "May I please have your attention? May I please have your attention!"

I looked to the front of the room and saw Elsie frantically pulling up her skirt over her white underpants. I poked Roy in the back. "What's going on? This some kind of striptease?"

Roy could only shake his head. He was laughing so hard tears wobbled in his eyes.

I turned to Diane. "What's going on?"

"When Elsie stood up, her skirt fell off," Diane answered me.

And then Jack let out a whoop.

This did it for Mrs. Hanson. She got her P.E. whistle out of her desk and blew it sharply. The room quieted.

"That is absolutely enough! I am ashamed of this class. Elsie . . ."

But it was too late to say anything to Elsie. She bunched the top of her skirt with one hand and pulled the classroom door open with the other. The door slammed behind her.

"Take out your arithmetic books and do page 360," Mrs. Hanson ordered. Page 360 was in the back of the book with solid pages of exercises.

"The whole page?" Roy asked.

"The whole page," Mrs. Hanson said firmly.

Slowly we all took out our books and paper and pencils. Diane stared at Mrs. Hanson hatefully. "She just likes to see us work."

"For talking, you may do page 360 *and* 361, Diane," Mrs. Hanson told her.

I could see Diane draw air into her chest, getting ready to object, but the cross look on Mrs. Hanson's face changed her mind.

Page 360 was solid multiplication. Two numbers times four numbers. It was going to take all day. I hadn't even seen what happened, and I had to do forty-two problems. Mrs. Hanson gave me a pain. When I was on problem 3, she tapped me on the shoulder.

"Jenifer, will you please go to the girls' lavatory and see if Elsie is all right," she whispered to me.

Elsie was slumped against the wall at the end of the sinks. Her head was tipped back and her face tilted up. Tears were streaming from her eyes, but she didn't bother to brush them away. One hand hung at her side. The other still clutched her skirt. She looked sad and hopeless and alone.

I had never thought of Elsie as a human being. Just a fat girl.

"Are you O.K.?" I asked her. "Mrs. Hanson wanted me to see if you're O.K."

Elsie closed her eyes. The tears dripped from under her eyelids.

I stood there for a while. "I'll go get a safety pin from Mrs. Hanson so you can pin up your skirt."

Elsie didn't answer.

The classroom was silent. Everyone's head was bent over an arithmetic book. I tiptoed up to Mrs. Hanson's desk.

"Can I have a safety pin for Elsie's skirt?"

"Certainly," she said and messed around in her top drawer until she found one.

When I returned to Elsie, she still had her eyes closed. I held out the pin. "Here. You can fix your skirt."

Elsie didn't seem to hear. She slid down the wall to the floor and sat there in a huge lump, her head drooping over her lap, tears falling onto her skirt.

I went into one of the stalls, came out, and fiddled with my hair in the mirror. She was still crying. I sat down on the floor beside her. "Elsie, it isn't that bad."

"What do you care?" she asked.

"Well, I don't want to see you cry."

"Then get out of here."

"No. Hey, Elsie, come on. Let's fix your skirt." I reached for her hand.

She pulled it away. "What do you care, Jenifer? Everyone likes you."

"Some people like you, too."

"Who?"

"Well . . . your mother and your sister and your friends."

"Not my mother, not my sister, and I don't have any friends." Elsie wiped her nose with her arm.

I got her a paper towel. "Somebody liked you once."

"No, they didn't. One person. Once my daddy did. That was five years ago."

I searched around in my head for something encouraging. "The kids will forget about this in a couple of days."

"So what?" Elsie's tears started coming again. "They all hate me. You hate me, too."

"No, I don't, Elsie. I did, but I don't now. I guess I didn't think about your having feelings."

Elsie's mouth drooped down on both sides. She stared ahead of her at the stall doors. I couldn't think of anything more to say. There was no point in trying to lie to her and say all the kids would learn to like her. Because they didn't and they wouldn't and she knew it.

Elsie heaved a shuddering sigh. "None of it matters anyway. I'll only be at this school a couple more months."

"Is your family moving away?"

"No, *I* am."

"How come?"

"Because the principal said I could just stay till the end of the school year on probation, and my mother doesn't want me anyway so she's sending me to a boarding school next fall."

"Maybe if you're good she'll change her mind."

"No, she won't. She wrote for all the boarding school pamphlets after I got caught with the licorice whips."

"She could still change her mind."

Elsie didn't bother to answer. We sat there beside each other, silently.

"Elsie," I said, "I'll be your friend."

She turned her head slowly to look at me. "What for?"

"Because I want to."

"Why do you want a thief for a friend? Why do you want a fat slob who sits and stuffs her face?"

"I'm sorry I said those things. Can we be friends?" I smiled cheerfully at her.

She did not smile back. "As soon as you stop feeling sorry for me, you won't want to be seen with me."

"Are you girls all right?" It was Mrs. Hanson at the door.

I scrambled up. Elsie lugged herself up, holding onto her skirt.

"Here, Jenifer," Mrs. Hanson said briskly, "give me the pin and I'll fix Elsie's skirt. You go on back to class."

I felt things were unfinished between us so I lingered a minute, but Mrs. Hanson turned her back on me and started pinning Elsie's waistband.

At recess the kids clotted up into groups and began going over Elsie. I noticed Marianne back off toward the tetherball and start swinging it by herself. She was the only one who cared about Elsie's feelings.

"Why are we all standing around raking over Elsie?" I demanded. "What's so interesting about this?"

Sharon looked at me, surprised. "Skirts don't fall off every day in school, you know, Jenny."

"Well, how would you like yours to fall off? How would you like the whole class laughing at you?"

"I don't spend all my time eating," Sharon told me.

"Her skirt didn't fall off because she was eating," I informed Sharon. "It fell off because she wasn't eating."

"You mean because she *couldn't* eat," Diane put in.

"That's right," I said. "She gets jailed in the office every recess . . . for the whole semester! I never heard of anyone getting punished that long. Did you ever hear of anyone getting punished that long in this school, Sharon?"

"I never heard of anyone stealing so much." Sharon was getting mad.

"O.K., so she did. She can change. I remember you wet the bed in third grade and you were afraid of sleeping over at Diane's house. Do you still wet the bed, Sharon?"

Sharon's face turned bright pink. Her nostrils turned white. She was really mad now. I stalked over to the tetherball and asked Marianne if she wanted to play.

I felt bad the rest of the day. I didn't want to fight with my friends. I didn't want Sharon to be mad. I didn't want to take that report card home. I watched Elsie sitting at her desk reading and yanking on her hair. It was an ugly, ugly day!

Getting to Know You

by Oscar Hammerstein II

Getting to know you,
Getting to know all about you.
Getting to like you,
Getting to hope you like me.

Getting to know you,
Putting it my way, but nicely.
You are precisely
My cup of tea!

Getting to know you,
Getting to feel free and easy.
When I am with you,
Getting to know what to say.

Haven't you noticed?
Suddenly I'm bright and breezy
Because of all the beautiful and new
Things I'm learning about you
Day
By
Day.

from

HOCKEYBAT HARRIS

by Geoffrey Bilson

In 1942, during the Second World War, a number of British children were sent to Canada to escape the bombing of their country. In this story Bob, who has always wanted a brother, has just been told that a boy from London, England, is coming to stay with his family.

Aunt Peg served the apple pie and ice cream and poured coffee for herself and Mrs. Williams. Bob ate happily, his mind full of plans for showing off his new brother. He imagined the two of them arriving at school on Monday morning, and everyone crowding round to meet the new kid. "Yeah, this is my new brother," he would say casually.

"Mum, what's his name? You never told us his name!"

"It's David Harris."

"He will be going to Albert, won't he?"

"Oh, yes, all the guest children go to the local school."

"Swell."

"Questions, questions," Mrs. Williams laughed. "Any more?"

"Where will he sleep, mum? Auntie Peg's using the spare room."

"I know." There was a pause. "He'll have to share your room."

That was a shock. Bob had never thought that when his brother moved into the house he would move into Bob's room. Bob toyed with the last forkful of pie on his plate.

"My room's awfully small, mum. And there's only one bed; will you be getting another?"

"Of course not. You'll only have to share until Aunt Peg goes to Halifax. That won't be so hard."

"Two of us in one bed," Bob said doubtfully.

"For goodness sake, child, lots of children share a bed. Just think of it as doing your bit for the war effort."

"It'll be fine, Bob," Aunt Peg said. "You're good at getting on with people—you'll manage."

"Yeah, I suppose so, Auntie."

"It'll be like a sleepover," Mrs. Williams said brightly, "only you boys had better not plan on talking until midnight every night."

"Well, not every night, mum."

Bob was lying on the floor listening to the hockey game when Mr. Williams arrived home. His father came into the living room carrying his supper on a tray and settled down in the big chair by the radio.

"Who's ahead?"

"The Leafs, dad—one up on Detroit."

"Good. This year we'll get the cup, right?"

"Hope so, dad. I couldn't take another series like last year."

The two of them had listened to the game every Saturday night for years. They both supported the Leafs and had been shattered when their team lost the Stanley Cup after three overtime defeats in the finals. Bob always sprawled on the floor, resting his chin on his hands. His feet now touched a small table near the wall that they had not reached last season and he enjoyed the feeling of being that much taller. Halfway into the second period, the doorbell rang. Mrs. Williams hurried from the kitchen to open the door. A wave of cold air rolled through the room, and Bob shivered and rose to his knees.

"Come on in. Don't stand around outside."

As Mrs. Smith came into the room, Mr. Williams stood up, and turned the radio down. He helped her take off her snow-covered coat. When Mr. Williams stepped aside, Bob suddenly saw a small boy standing a step behind Mrs. Smith. It was almost as though Mr. Williams had done a conjuring trick, producing the boy with a shake of Mrs. Smith's coat. That made Bob laugh and the boy flushed.

"Here, Bob, take David's suitcase and say hello. David, give me that wet coat. Come on in and get warm," Mrs. Williams said, taking

David's coat and scarf and half pushing him into the living room.

"Hi, David," Bob said.

"Hello," David walked slowly into the room, looking around as if he hoped to see something familiar. His hair stood up at the back of his head where he had pulled off his toque. His large ears were red with cold.

Bob went to pick up the suitcase. Strapped on the outside was a bat with a long blade, flat on one side and wedged shaped on the other. It had a long handle covered in red rubber.

"Hey, is that a cricket bat?" Bob asked.

"Of course it is," David snapped. "What does it look like?"

There was a silence; the tiny voice of Foster Hewitt crackled from the radio and the crowd cheered. Mr. Williams turned the radio off.

"Well, we don't play too much cricket around here, David, not at this time of year. It's mostly hockey."

"I don't have a hockeybat."

Bob laughed and the four adults all smiled. David turned bright red.

"I mean stick. Everyone knows it's a stick. Hockey's a stupid girls' game. Jolly hockey sticks," he shouted.

"It's okay, David," Aunt Peg said. "There's no need to get upset over a little slip of the tongue. It just sounded a bit funny to us, that's all."

David glowered for a moment, relaxed and then said, "I'm sorry. I shouldn't fly off the handle like that."

"Why is everyone standing around?" Mr. Williams said. "Mrs. Smith, sit down, and you too, Mary. I'll get you some coffee. Bob, take that case upstairs. You must be starving, David. Come into the kitchen and we'll fix you some bacon and eggs."

Bob carried the case upstairs, and turned on the light in his room. It looked very small. The big bed took up a lot of space. When Bob put the suitcase down at the foot of the bed there was not much room to spare. "Well, he's here now," Bob thought and laughed to himself as he remembered the hockeybat.

from

Bridge to Terabithia

by Katherine Paterson

Jess and Leslie ran up over the empty field behind the old Perkins place and down to the dry creek bed that separated farmland from the woods. There was an old crab apple tree there, just at the bank of the creek bed, from which someone long forgotten had hung a rope.

They took turns swinging across the gully on the rope. It was a glorious autumn day, and if you looked up as you swung, it gave you the feeling of floating. Jess leaned back and drank in the rich, clear colour of the sky. He was drifting, drifting like a fat white lazy cloud back and forth across the blue.

"Do you know what we need?" Leslie called to him. Intoxicated as he was with the heavens, he couldn't imagine needing anything on earth.

"We need a place," she said, "just for us. It would be so secret that we would never tell anyone in the whole world about it." Jess came swinging back and dragged his feet to stop. She lowered her voice almost to a whisper. "It might be a whole secret country," she continued, "and you and I would be the rulers of it."

Her words stirred inside of him. He'd like to be a ruler of something. Even something that wasn't real. "O.K.," he said. "Where could we have it?"

"Over there in the woods where nobody would come and mess it up."

There were parts of the woods that Jess did not like. Dark places where it was almost like being under water, but he didn't say so.

"I know"—she was getting excited—"it could be a magic country like Narnia, and the only way you can get in is by swinging across on this enchanted rope." Her eyes were bright. She grabbed the rope. "Come on," she said. "Let's find a place to build our castle stronghold."

They had gone only a few yards into the woods beyond the creek bed when Leslie stopped.

"How about right here?" she asked.

"Sure," Jess agreed quickly, relieved that there was no need to plunge deeper into the woods. He would take her there, of course, for he wasn't such a coward that he would mind a little exploring now and then farther in amongst the ever-darkening columns of the tall pines. But as a regular thing, as a permanent place, this was where he would choose to be—here where the dogwood and redbud played hide and seek between the oaks and evergreens, and the sun flung itself in golden streams through the trees to splash warmly at their feet.

"Sure," he repeated himself, nodding vigorously. The underbrush was dry and would be easy to clear away. The ground was almost level. "This'll be a good place to build."

Leslie named their secret land "Terabithia," and she loaned Jess all of her books about Narnia, so he would know how things went in a magic kingdom—how the animals and the trees must be protected and how a ruler must behave. That was the hard part. When Leslie spoke, the words rolling out so regally, you knew she was a proper queen. He could hardly manage English, much less the poetic language of a king.

But he could make stuff. They dragged boards and other materials down from the scrap heap by Miss Bessie's pasture and built their castle stronghold in the place they had found in the woods. Leslie filled a three-pound coffee can with crackers and dried fruit and a one-pound can with strings and nails. They found five old Pepsi bottles which they washed and filled with water, in case, as Leslie said, "of siege."

Like God in the Bible, they looked at what they had made and found it very good.

"You should draw a picture of Terabithia for us to hang in the castle," Leslie said.

"I can't." How could he explain it in a way Leslie would understand, how he yearned to reach out and capture the quivering life about him and how when he tried, it slipped past his fingertips, leaving a dry fossil upon the page? "I just can't get the poetry of the trees," he said.

She nodded. "Don't worry," she said. "You will someday."

He believed her because there in the shadowy light of the stronghold everything seemed possible. Between the two of them they owned the world and no enemy, Gary Fulcher, Wanda Kay Moore, Janice Avery, Jess's own fears and insufficiencies, nor any of the foes whom Leslie imagined attacking Terabithia, could ever really defeat them.

A few days after they finished the castle, Janice Avery fell down in the school bus and yelled that Jess had tripped her as she went past. She made such a fuss that Mrs. Prentice, the driver, ordered Jess off the bus, and he had to walk the three miles home.

When Jess finally got to Terabithia, Leslie was huddled next to one of the cracks below the roof trying to get enough light to read. There was a picture on the cover which showed a killer whale attacking a dolphin.

"Whatcha doing?" He came in and sat beside her on the ground.

"Reading. I had to do something. That girl!" Her anger came rocketing to the surface.

"It don't matter. I don't mind walking all that much." What was a little hike compared to what Janice Avery might have chosen to do?

"It's the *principle* of the thing, Jess. That's what you've got to understand. You have to stop people like that. Otherwise they turn into tyrants and dictators."

He reached over and took the whale book from her hands,

pretending to study the bloody picture on the jacket. "Getting any good ideas?"

"What?"

"I thought you was getting some ideas on how to stop Janice Avery."

"No, stupid. We're trying to *save* the whales. They might become extinct."

He gave her back the book. "You save the whales and shoot the people, huh?"

She grinned finally. "Something like that, I guess. Say, did you ever hear the story about Moby Dick?"

"Who's that?"

"Well, there was once this huge white whale named Moby Dick. . . ." And Leslie began to spin out a wonderful story about a whale and a crazy sea captain who was bent on killing it. His fingers itched to try to draw it on paper. Maybe if he had some proper paints, he could do it. There ought to be a way of making the whale shimmering white against the dark water.

Terabithia was cold in November. They didn't dare build a fire in the castle, though sometimes they would build one outside and huddle around it. For a while Leslie had been able to keep two sleeping bags in the stronghold, but around the first of December her father noticed their absence, and she had to take them back. Actually, Jess made her take them back. It was not that he was afraid of the Burkes exactly. Leslie's parents were young, with straight white teeth and lots of hair—both of them. Leslie called them Judy and Bill, which bothered Jess more than he wanted it to. It was none of his business what Leslie called her parents. But he just couldn't get used to it.

Both of the Burkes were writers. Mrs. Burke wrote novels and, according to Leslie, was more famous than Mr. Burke, who wrote about politics. It was really something to see the shelf that had their books on it. Mrs. Burke was "Judith Hancock" on the cover, which threw you at first, but then if you looked on the back, there was her picture looking very young and serious. Mr. Burke was going back and forth to Washington to finish a book he was working on with someone else, but he had promised Leslie that after Christmas he would stay home and fix up the house and plant his garden and listen to music and read books out loud and write only in his spare time.

They didn't look like Jess's idea of rich, but even he could tell that the jeans they wore had not come off the counter at Newberry's. There was no TV at the Burkes', but there were mountains of records and a stereo set that looked like something off *Star Trek*. And although their car was small and dusty, it was Italian and looked expensive, too.

They were always nice to Jess when he went over, but then they would suddenly begin talking about French politics or string quartets (which he at first thought was a square box made out of string), or how to save the timber wolves or redwoods or singing whales, and he was scared to open his mouth and show once and for all how dumb he was.

He wasn't comfortable having Leslie at his house either. Joyce Ann would stare, her index finger pulling down her mouth and

making her drool. Brenda and Ellie always managed some remark about "*girl* friend." His mother acted stiff and funny just the way she did when she had to go up to school about something. Later she would refer to Leslie's "tacky" clothes. Leslie always wore pants, even to school. Her hair was "shorter than a boy's." Her parents were "hardly more than hippies." May Belle either tried to push in with him and Leslie or sulked at being left out. His father had seen Leslie only a few times and had nodded to show that he had noticed her, but his mother said that she was sure he was fretting that his only son did nothing but play with girls, and they both were worried about what would become of it.

Jess didn't concern himself with what would "become of it." For the first time in his life he got up every morning with something to look forward to. Leslie was more than his friend. She was his other, more exciting self—his way to Terabithia and all the worlds beyond.

Terabithia was their secret, which was a good thing, for how could Jess have ever explained it to an outsider? Just walking down the hill toward the woods made something warm and liquid steal through his body. The closer he came to the dry creek bed and the crab apple tree rope the more he could feel the beating of his heart. He grabbed the end of the rope and swung out toward the other bank with a kind of wild exhilaration and landed gently on his feet, taller and stronger and wiser in that mysterious land.

Leslie's favourite place besides the castle stronghold was the pine forest. There the trees grew so thick at the top that the sunshine was veiled. No low bush or grass could grow in that dim light, so the ground was carpeted with golden needles.

"I used to think this place was haunted," Jess had confessed to Leslie the first afternoon he had revved up his courage to bring her there.

"Oh, but it is," she said. "But you don't have to be scared. It's not haunted with evil things."

"How do you know?"

"You can just feel it. Listen."

At first he heard only the stillness. It was the stillness that had

always frightened him before, but this time it was like the moment after Miss Edmunds finished a song, just after the chords hummed down to silence. Leslie was right. They stood there, not moving, not wanting the swish of dry needles beneath their feet to break the spell. Far away from their former world came the cry of geese heading southward.

Leslie took a deep breath. "This is not an ordinary place," she whispered. "Even the rulers of Terabithia come into it only at times of greatest sorrow or of greatest joy. We must strive to keep it sacred. It would not do to disturb the Spirits."

He nodded, and without speaking, they went back to the creek bank where they shared together a solemn meal of crackers and dried fruit.

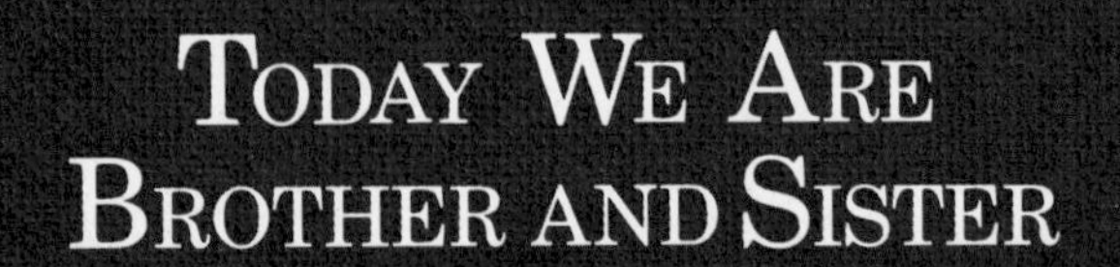

Today We Are Brother and Sister

by Arnold Adoff

Brother:

Get your rotten sneaker off my pants,
and stop shaking the sand on
my bed! You took the last piece of
toast, and now you go
to
the grocery for a loaf
of bread.

Sister:

You left your wet towel on the floor
again, you brat, and knocked
my cards down
from the shelf. Now
get
them back together!
Don't
you care about a person's
property . . . ?

Together:

Brother on the beach.
Sister
on the sand.
Rolling
in the water.
Strolling
hand
in
hand.

Sister sand
and brother
beach:
together
each,
together
each.
Reach.
Reach.
R e a c h.

Sister:

Put a little water in your mask and shake
it all around, then it won't fog up
so much. When your snorkel tube
goes under
water,
don't forget
to blow real hard and empty it.
And don't swallow.

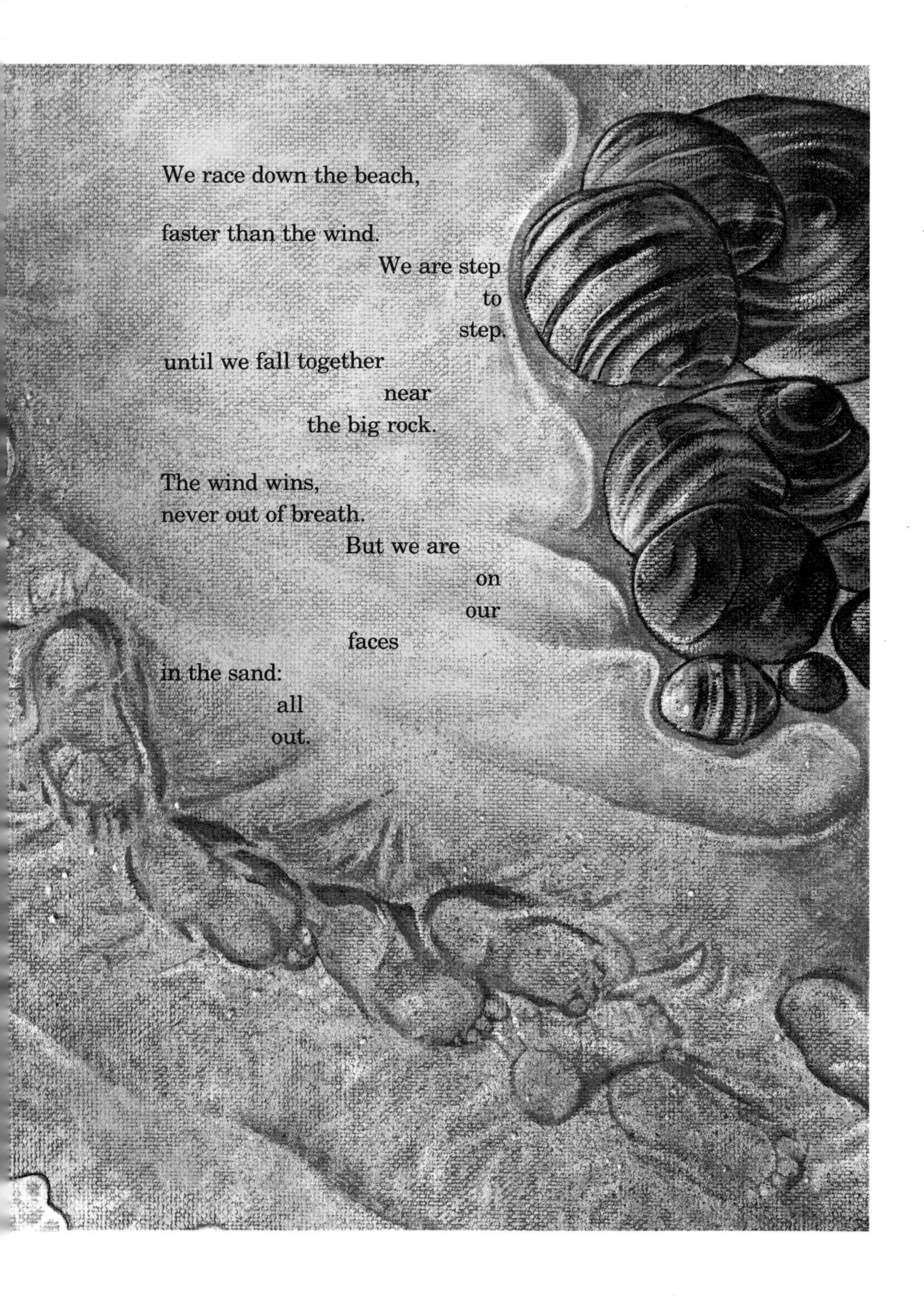

We race down the beach,

faster than the wind.
We are step
to
step.
until we fall together
near
the big rock.

The wind wins,
never out of breath.
But we are
on
our
faces
in the sand:
all
out.

from

A TASTE OF BLACKBERRIES

by Doris Buchanan Smith

Mrs. Houser was holding Jamie's baby brother and Martha sat on the floor with a colouring book and crayons. Everything was dark and cool. Jamie's mother said the house was cooler if it was closed up.

"I'll take the children," Mom said to Mrs. Houser. Mrs. Houser handed over the baby.

"Son, help Martha gather up her crayons and take her over to our playroom."

"Jamie got stung," Martha said, barely looking up from her colouring. I reached under her armpits and pulled her to her feet. We left Mom and Mrs. Houser talking in hushed tones.

Martha dropped her crayons in the middle of the yard and we both stooped over to pick them up. I stuffed as many as I could into my pockets.

"That's the colour of the am-blance," Martha said, holding the white crayon. "Did you see it? Did you see Jamie get a ride?" Her eyes were bright and excited. We were almost at the spot where the ambulance had parked.

"Yeah," I grunted. I guess I was the only kid in the neighbourhood who hadn't been impressed by that ambulance. The whole neighbourhood was running and squealing to see what was the matter.

That Jamie. He was an expert attention getter, even when, maybe, he didn't intend to be. I wondered briefly if he had been faking unconsciousness just to keep from grinning at all of us. It would serve him right if he was out cold and didn't even know he was riding in an ambulance.

Something in my conscience kicked me. What if something really was badly wrong. Naw, it couldn't be. What could happen to Jamie the Great? He yelled a lot, but he was tough.

If we were wrestling, he would scream sometimes so I thought I had really hurt him, but he would never give up, never. And he

would do such crazy comic falls that you'd wonder how he kept from breaking his neck. Jamie was a show-off and a clown all right, there was no doubt about that. And most of the time it was funny.

I stretched out on the playroom floor and coloured a picture for Martha. She could colour pretty good for four. She didn't stay inside the lines very well, but the colours she used looked good together. I mean, she didn't dress a lady in black and purple. I coloured my entire picture in shades of green and Martha was very impressed.

Mother came in with the baby and I stayed on the floor and started another picture. Part of me wanted to find out all about Jamie; but the other part was afraid to hear.

She laid the baby on the sofa and pushed a chair against it. The baby was asleep, all roses and cream. If I could put that colour into a crayon it would be a miracle.

When Mom had the baby settled she called softly for me to come with her. She sat down at the kitchen table and motioned for me to sit down. I couldn't sit. Some awful instinct was hammering on my brain. I tried not to listen.

"Jamie is dead, darling," she said.

"Dead darling" rang in my head. Jamie is dead, darling. Jamie is dead darling. He didn't look so darling flopping around on the ground, showing off. Jamie was a freak.

"I know," I said bluntly. "I saw the ambulance." I felt trapped. I didn't want to listen to her telling me lies about Jamie.

"Were you out there when it happened?"

"Yes."

"What happened?"

"Jamie poked a stick down a bee hole."

"Did you get stung?"

"No. I stood still."

"Then what happened?"

"Everybody ran."

"Did Jamie run?"

It was as though she had punched me in the stomach. I saw Jamie again, falling down and writhing. I closed my eyes. I shouldn't have left. I should have helped him. But how could I know? I swallowed. I thought I was going to be sick.

"Did Jamie run?" she repeated.

"No," I said. "He fell down. I thought he was faking."

She reached out to touch me but I was out of reach and didn't move closer.

"I know," she said. "We all know how Jamie was."

My mind buzzed like that swarm of bees. I hadn't even got stung, and Jamie was dead. Someone had got stung eleven times and it was just like giant mosquito bites, and Jamie was dead.

"How many times was he stung?" I asked. He must have been stung a hundred times.

"Just once or twice. It wasn't the number of stings, it was that Jamie was allergic to them. A few people are allergic to bee stings."

Allergic? I knew about that. A girl at school was allergic to chocolate. It made her sick. We all felt sorry for her. But I didn't know that being allergic could kill you.

"Did Jamie know he was allergic to bee stings?"

"No, he didn't, sweetheart. No one did. He wouldn't have played around a bee hole if he had. It was a freak accident. It hardly ever happens."

"How did they—? Who found him?"

"Mrs. Houser. She looked out to see if you were all working and she saw Jamie on the ground. She ran over and got Jamie's mother."

Mrs. Houser! I would have thought she'd just let you lie there and rot.

"I'm going upstairs," I announced. I went to my room and stood by the window, staring out. Did the world know that Jamie was dead? The sky didn't act like it. It was a blue-sky and white-cloud day. Horses and lambs and floppy-eared dogs chased across the sky. Was Jamie playing with them?

What kinds of things could you do when you were dead? Or was dead just plain dead and that's all?

I looked across at Jamie's window. He would never flash me a signal again. We had learned Morse code, Jamie and I, and talked

to each other at night. Before that we had taken cans and a string and stretched it across from his window to mine.

That had been a funny day. It had been so easy to string up one can and drop the string down from Jamie's window. It wasn't so easy getting the string up to my window.

We dragged the string across the street and Jamie tried to throw the can up to me. I was a little scornful of Jamie's pitching arm until I tried it myself with him upstairs trying to catch.

Finally, I climbed my mother's rose trellis by the kitchen window, careful to keep my foot at the cross pieces of the trellis where it was strongest. I picked my way up through the thorns until I was on the sun deck with the can and string.

"Yeah, smarty," Jamie laughed. "Now, how are you going to get it to your room?"

We felt like engineers trying to set up a communications system, but we figured it out. Then the dumb thing didn't work! We just flopped down exhausted.

"And you know what I just thought of?" Jamie asked when he came back over. "Why didn't we just drop an extra piece of string from your window and tie it onto this one and pull it up?" It was so simple we collapsed again and clapped our arms over our heads. We felt so stupid.

Later, we had got the encyclopedia and looked up Morse code. We saved our money and bought flashlights with blinker buttons. It certainly was easier than that stupid set of cans. And it worked.

So, my mother had told me that Jamie was dead. No more blinks from across the street at night. No more Jamie. Who would we have to make us laugh anymore?

THE TWELVE DAYS OF CHRISTMAS NORTH

by Lois Barber

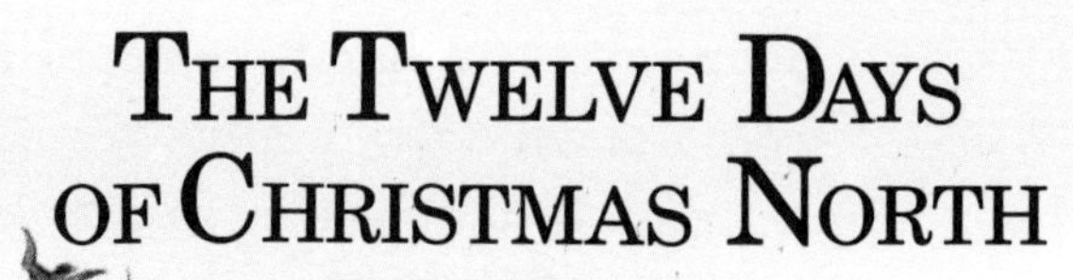

On the twelfth day of Christmas my true love sent to me . . .

twelve whales a'playing

eleven foxes frisking

ten ravens calling

nine eagles soaring

eight wolves a'howling

seven salmon leaping

six beavers swimming

five mountain goats

four grizzly bears

three bull moose

two porcupines and

a blue grouse in a spruce tree.

from
Honor Bound

by Mary Alice and John Downie

Miles laid an icy hand on Patience's cheek. "Get dressed! Have you forgotten? It's Christmas. The Tricks are coming for dinner and Mama wants decorations." Miles had already gathered an armload of bittersweet and handed her a spray of the bright red berries. "We'll need more of these and pine boughs and cones too."

Patience scrambled hastily into her dress. Papa called it her frock of many colours, for Mama had sewn every imaginable kind of fur upon it: squirrel, bear, rabbit, deer, muskrat, and beaver. Patience loved it dearly and felt like an Indian princess whenever she wore it. Miles said she was such a prickly character it should be made of porcupine quills, but she had learned to ignore his teasing—most of the time.

As Mama gave her breakfast Patience saw that a kettle of pea soup was already simmering on the fire; there were two loaves of bread growing brown and crusty in the ashes. Mama had paid close attention to her baking lessons with Mrs Trick.

Miles and Patience worked all morning, attended by Hodge, who nearly got stepped on several times. Mama made a large evergreen wreath and Papa dragged in a yule log. He sniffed the air appreciatively. "Pea soup, pine boughs, and freshly baked bread. I would not exchange such fragrances for all the perfumes of Araby. When do the Tricks arrive?"

Branches festooned the walls and twined around the stump-table. The bittersweet berries glowed on the shelf, in the centre of the table, and even on top of the clock. Patience had made a collar of berries for an indignant Hodge. She spent the last hour going to the door and looking out hopefully for the Tricks. "They'll never come," she said.

"Perhaps a bear—" Miles was interrupted by voices.

"Wassail, wassail, out of the milk pail,
Wassail, wassail, in snow, frost and hail,
Wassail, wassail, with partridge and rail,
Wassail, wassail, that never will fail."

Papa opened the door and there stood all the Tricks beaming.

"I always say, Christmas dinner is a time to cram and stuff as much as you like," said Mrs Trick, handing Mama a venison pie, an enormous bilberry currant tart, and a bottle of red currant wine. Sam and Mr Trick followed her in, their arms laden with baskets.

They began their celebration with a Christmas service. Sam read the lesson while his parents gazed admiringly. They sang "While shepherds watched their flocks by night," and Mama sang the "Cherry tree Carol," which had been Honor's favourite.

Later they sat down to a dinner that satisfied even Mrs Trick with the number and variety of its dishes. There was wild roast turkey with cranberry jelly, wild pigeons and fish, venison pie, honey and squash, and pumpkin bread. Then they had Mrs Trick's tart for dessert. They ate and talked happily while Mama and Mrs Trick kept refilling the wooden bowls and mugs.

"A feast fit for a bashaw with nine tails, eh, my bald-headed eaglet?" said Mr Trick to his wife. At that moment he caught sight of Hodge, who was pecking crumbs from the floor.

"What's that bird doing here?" he asked.

"It's my bluejay," Patience told him.

Mr Trick looked at Hodge with disapproval. "I don't hold with birds, except in pies," he said, "ever since I was a little boy in England and had to act as a crowherd to keep the pests out of the garden." In a high falsetto voice he piped:

"Away, away, away birds;
Take a little bit and come another day, birds;
Great birds, little birds, pigeons and crows,
I'll up with my clackers and down she goes."

"Now for some Christmas pie," said Mr Trick with a twinkle from beneath his eyebrows, and Sam produced a huge pie from the bag in which Mrs Trick had brought her share of the provisions.

"We are in danger of being over-venisoned and over-pigeoned," protested Papa, belching comfortably. Sam handed Patience his jackknife with a flourish, and she plunged it eagerly into the crust. What would appear? Plums, berries, or some of Mrs Trick's precious apples, brought from Cataraqui and hoarded during the winter?

"Four-and-twenty blackbirds baked in a pie," sang Mr Trick, glancing at Hodge.

The knife cut through air. "You're joking me," Patience said. "There's nothing in it."

"Hidden treasure!" Sam whispered.

"Come now, don't tease," said Mrs Trick. "Lift off the crust."

Sam did so and revealed a pie full of presents. For Mama there was a cherry rolling-pin. It was extra long and the red-brown wood had been polished to a satiny-smooth finish.

"What huge pies I shall make with this," said Mama. "Pies to satisfy the appetite of a Grimble!"

For Miles there was a deerskin sheath filled with arrows. The birchbark case for pens could only have been meant for Papa. And nestled at the bottom of the pie there was a soft warm squirrel-skin bonnet. Despite the heat and stuffiness of the crowded room, Patience put it on at once and sat blissfully roasting.

"How very kind," began Mama, "but—"

"Pish, tush," said Mrs Trick briskly. " 'Tis but a token of gratitude for teaching our Sammy to be a scholar."

The wolves were howling in the distance when the Tricks began to say good night and put on their cloaks and coats to go home.

"Perhaps you should pass the night here," said Mama, trying to think where she would put everyone. Mr Trick picked up a thick stick that he had left by the door and twirled it menacingly.

"No wolf need think that it will befrighten *me* with the sight of it," he said. "Bless you all. Good night."

from

From Anna

by Jean Little

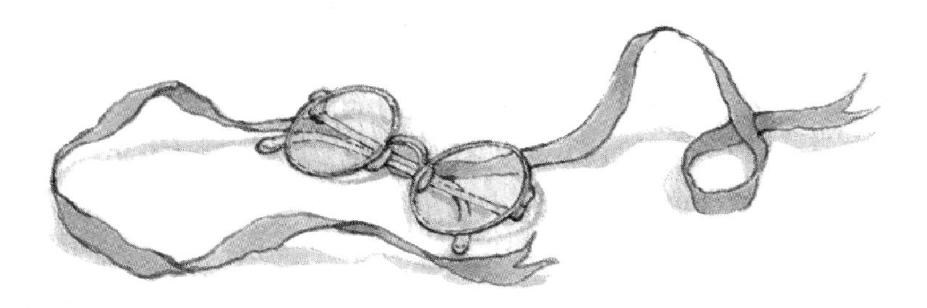

It is during the Great Depression and the Solden children are holding a meeting to discuss Christmas presents for their parents. The youngest, Anna, who has been placed in a special Sight Saving Class because of her poor vision, arrives home from school to hear her brother, Rudi, announcing his idea to the others.

"This year, we'll make our presents for them and save them the Christmas money Papa always hands out. When they go to give it to you, Gretchen, you can just say. 'Thank you, but this time we have decided to make our own arrangements.' "

While Gretchen practised the words over in an airy unreal voice and Anna leaned over to unbuckle her galoshes, the twins clamoured for attention.

"But, Rudi, we're no good at making things."

Anna felt a sudden chill. She worked on the next buckle. It was stiff. What would Rudi say?

"Can you earn money?" Rudi wanted to know.

"Well . . . maybe," Fritz ventured for them both.

"Buy them something, then," Rudi lightly brushed aside their anxiety. He was not going to have anyone or anything stand in the way of his plan. "That's what I'm going to do myself."

"How?"

"You'll see. I promise you one thing though. It's going to be the best present of them all," boasted Rudi.

Anna kicked her overshoes off. The other four turned at the

sound and discovered her. She watched, while dismay broke over each face in turn.

"What in the world can Anna give them?" Gretchen was the one who put it into words.

"Oh, she doesn't count. She's only nine," Rudi said too quickly. Staring up at the ceiling, suddenly he started to whistle.

He was wrong about her not counting. With Ben she counted. With Isobel. With Papa. With Miss Williams. Anna knew that. But the words still flicked at her in a way that hurt.

Still, could she make a Christmas present for her parents? Rudi could earn money easily. He said so himself. And Gretchen knitted almost as well as Mama. The twins, Anna was sure, would find a way.

They are full of imagination, she thought.

She alone could do nothing.

"You really are mean, Rudi," Gretchen flared. "Of course Anna will want to give something. And I will so knit her something. If it's from Anna, it needn't be anything big or special."

The last sentence jabbed into Anna like the thrust of a knife. Suddenly, she stopped thinking. Her chin shot up. Her eyes, behind her big glasses, sparked with anger and humiliation. They would see. She would show them.

"I will give my own present, thank you very much, Lady Gretchen," she threw the words like darts. "You can keep your stupid knitting."

Then, before any of them could come back with a retort to remind her who she was—the youngest, the *Dummkopf*, Awkward Anna—she wheeled around and left the room.

At the top of the stairs, she veered and went to look at herself in the bathroom mirror. Anna was not interested in the sight of her own face. To her, it was dull and plain. She had never seen it when her dimples flashed. But she could talk to herself better sometimes when she could see herself at the same time.

"Can I make a present?" she asked the girl in the mirror. "How can I earn money? A lot of money!" she added recklessly.

She might as well make her wishes big.

But the girl in the mirror looked as discouraged as Anna felt. She hunched up her shoulders, made a face at herself, and turned away.

Papa might help, Anna thought suddenly.

But no.

This present had to be a surprise, a secret. It would not be fair to go to Papa.

Anna wandered into her alcove and lay on her cot. She did not search for an inspiration any longer. She just hoped. Maybe, somehow, something wonderful would happen yet.

They were going to make wastepaper baskets.

Anna stared uncertainly at the queer collection of things Miss Williams said they were going to need. There were circles and ovals of wood with holes drilled in a neatly spaced row around each edge. There were bundles of straight sticks, cream-coloured and clean. There were lengths of reed, rolled up and tied in bunches so they would not spring free and trail all over the room. Some of the reeds were flat and as wide as her finger. Some were round and thin like brittle brown twine.

It looked complicated. It looked much too hard for her to do by herself. Yet she had to do it on her own. The others were not having help.

Miss Williams did not look worried.

"I wish I had a finished basket to show you," she told the troubled faces grouped around her. "But it will be all right. I promise you."

Anna was comforted. She had never known the teacher to break a promise.

"Now let's begin," Miss Williams said.

First they had to choose the shape they wanted their baskets to be. Anna picked on an oval base. It looked good and big—she did not want to make a small present. She had just learned how to use a ruler. She took hers out of her desk and measured the piece of wood. It was six inches wide at the centre and ten inches long. Anna smiled and put the ruler back.

Next they put the reeds to soak in a bucket of water. Anybody could do that. Anna did it carefully, slowly. Josie hurried and broke one of her reeds.

"Treat them gently, Josie," Miss Williams warned. "Watch how Anna handles hers."

By the middle of the afternoon the reeds were pliable enough to weave. Anna put in the upright pegs first. They had to be even.

She placed each one slowly, coaxing it, guiding it through the correct hole, measuring first with her eyes and then with her ruler.

"That's it, Isobel. Good, Veronica," Miss Williams went from one to another. "Not so fast, Jimmy. They're uneven at the top."

She paused by Anna's desk. The others were getting ahead of Anna but she was paying no attention to that. She wanted this basket to be just right, like something Gretchen would make, or Mama.

"That's perfect, Anna," the teacher said.

Perfect!

Anna started to tuck in the ends, one behind the other, so that the underside of her basket would be trim and neat. It made an attractive pattern. She stopped to admire it.

"Let me see that," Isobel said, reaching for it. "Oh, I get it. Thanks, Anna."

She handed the basket back and bent her head over her own, undoing her mistake and fixing it. Anna blinked with surprise.

Then, intently, she listened as Miss Williams explained how to do the actual weaving of the reeds. It sounded almost easy. You started with the thin ones. Anna reached for a length of reed. Her hand shook.

Catch the end behind one of the uprights.

She did that. For an instant, she felt all thumbs. The reed slipped loose. Anna bit her lip and began again, more slowly. This time it stayed put. She took a deep breath, gathered her courage, and started to weave.

In and out, in and out. Each time she had to pull the whole long whip-end of reed all the way through. What seemed like yards and yards of it curled and coiled around her. There! She had done it.

Now pull it tight.

Not too tight, Anna reminded herself.

It must fit snugly around the straight sticks, but pulled too hard, it might break. She tugged at it until it felt exactly the way it should. She did not wonder how she was so certain. Her hands knew.

Miss Williams came to her again. There was not a mistake in the child's work. She was concentrating so intently that she was not even aware of the woman who stood watching her.

"How deft your fingers are, Anna!" Miss Williams said.

Anna's head jerked up. She stared at the teacher. What did "deft" mean?

"Deft means quick and clever," the teacher answered her unspoken question. "Sure of themselves."

Anna knew that up till that very moment, she had had clumsy hands.

"Let me do it, Anna," Mama or Gretchen or even Frieda had

often said impatiently. Rudi still called her Awkward Anna when he thought about it.

Now she had deft fingers.

Anna went on weaving the reeds around and around, over and under, over and under. As she worked deftly, neatly, nimbly, a new song was singing itself inside her heart.

A Christmas present,
I am making my Christmas present.
I am making my very own.
It will be from me.

A Christmas present,
A surprise for a Christmas present!
I am making it by myself
And Papa will see.

She had never known such joy. But Miss Williams made them stop long before they were finished.

"There is still something called Spelling," she told them dryly. "And Arithmetic, too, Jimmy."

The next day she gave them time to work on the baskets again, though. Slowly the sides rose. Anna finished with the narrow round reeds and began to weave the flat ones. In and out, in and out.

"My hand's tired," Josie complained. Her basket was messy too.

Anna's hand was not one bit tired. And her basket was not messy.

"She's pretty good for a kid, isn't she?" Bernard said to Miss Williams.

"Not just for a kid," Miss Williams answered. "Anna has a gift for taking infinite pains."

Even Bernard had to have that explained, though he had spoken English all his life.

I wish I could make him a present too, Anna thought. And Isobel and Ben . . . and Miss Williams . . . and Dr. Schumacher.

She could never do it. Not five more presents! She who had not even been able to make one until Miss Williams showed her how. But she thought about it, as her hands pulled the long reeds through and pushed them back. She thought and she began to see how she might.

The basket must be done first though. Her excitement mounted as she neared the end. When she was two inches from the top, she went back to the thin, round reeds. It was like making a border. Then, suddenly, it was complete. It stood almost a foot high. The sides slanted out a little, gracefully. (Several of the others had not been able to manage this. Theirs went straight up like stove pipes.) All the ends were tucked in out of sight. There were no gaps. Anna turned it around slowly, gloating over it.

"Take your pencils and print your initials on the bottom," Miss Williams instructed. "I have arranged to have them painted at the School for the Blind. I wouldn't want you to get them mixed up when they come back."

Anna laughed. As though she would ever confuse her basket with anybody else's! She printed her initials clearly on the white wood.

A.E.S.

Then the baskets were taken away.

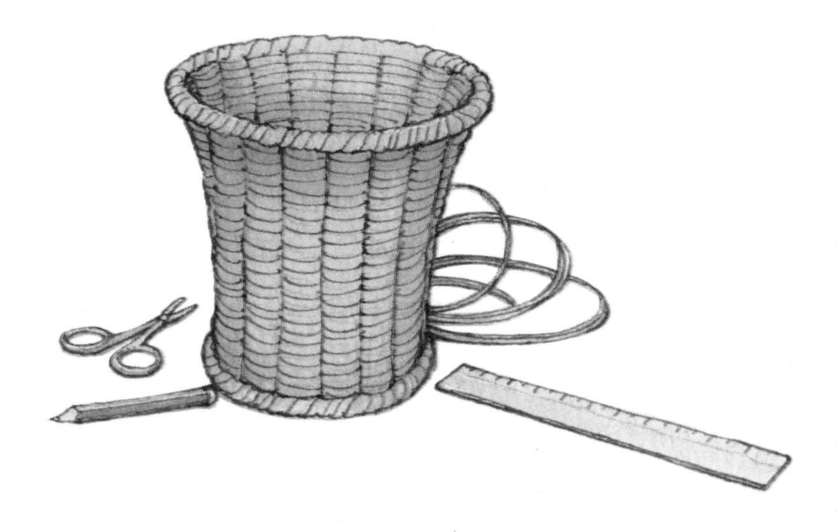

Going Through the Old Photos

by Michael Rosen

Me, my dad
and my brother
we were looking through the old photos.
Pictures of my dad with a broken leg
and my mum with big flappy shorts on
and me on a tricycle
when we got to one of my mum
with a baby on her knee,
and I go, "Is that me or Brian?"
And my dad says,
"Let's have a look.
It isn't you or Brian," he says.
"It's Alan.
He died. He would have been
two years younger
than Brian
and two years older than you.
He was a lovely baby."

"How did he die?"

"Whooping cough.
I was away at the time.
He coughed himself to death in Connie's arms.
The terrible thing is,
it wouldn't happen today,
but it was during the war, you see,
and they didn't have the medicines.
That must be the only photo
of him we've got."

Me and Brian
looked at the photo.
We couldn't say anything.
It was the first time we had ever heard about Alan.
For a moment I felt ashamed
like as if I had done something wrong.
I looked at the baby trying to work out
who he looked like.
I wanted to know what another brother
would have been like.
No way of saying.
And Mum looked so happy.
Of course she didn't know
when they took the photo
that he would die, did she?

Funny thing is,
though my father mentioned it every now and then
over the years,
Mum—never.
And he never said anything in front of her
about it
and we never let on that we knew.
What I've never figured out
was whether
her silence was because
she was more upset about it
than my dad—
or less.

AUTOGRAPH VERSES

I oughta smile
I oughta laugh
But in this book
I autograph!
from David

MAY YOUR LIFE BE
LIKE ARITHMETIC —
FRIENDS ADDED
JOYS MULTIPLIED
SORROWS SUBTRACTED
AND ENEMIES DIVIDED.
Elizabeth

What shall I write?
What shall it be?
Just two words
Remember me.
Love, Maria

Find new friends
But keep the old,
One is silver
The other gold.
Grant.

Forget you? No, I never can
As long as I can whistle.
I may as well forget to
scream
When I sit on a thistle.
Jorge

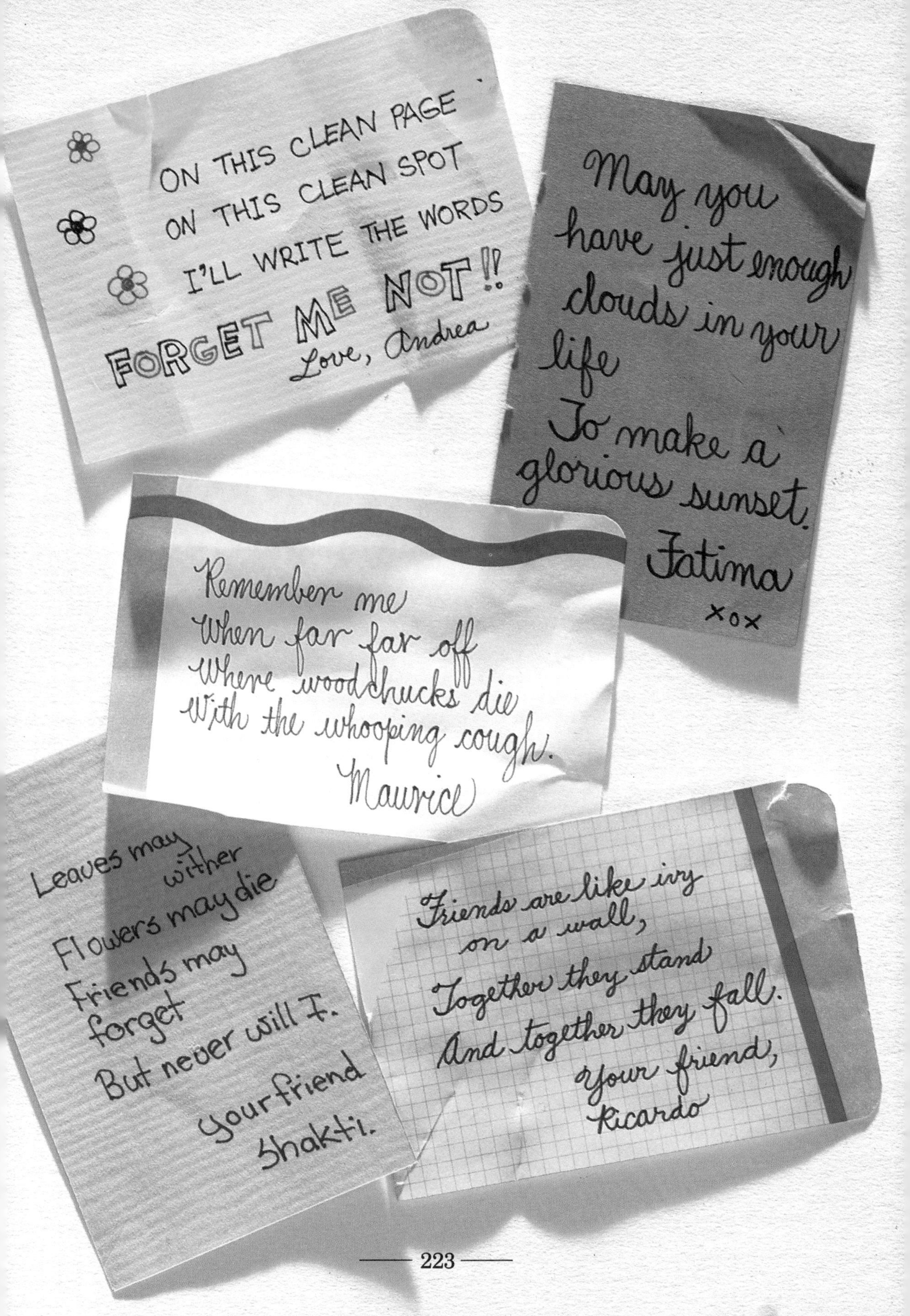

ON THIS CLEAN PAGE
ON THIS CLEAN SPOT
I'LL WRITE THE WORDS
FORGET ME NOT!!
Love, Andrea

May you
have just enough
clouds in your
life
To make a
glorious sunset.
Fatima
xox

Remember me
When far far off
Where woodchucks die
With the whooping cough.
Maurice

Leaves may
wither
Flowers may die
Friends may
forget
But never will I.
Your friend
Shakti.

Friends are like ivy
on a wall,
Together they stand
And together they fall.
Your friend,
Ricardo

The High Country

Even if they live in the most crowded of cities, people enjoy travelling into the land—camping, touring, visiting nature parks, birdwatching, or even going on safaris—in search of nature and animal life. What is it that attracts humans to animals? Humans may themselves be considered animals in some ways, but they still find something very special about leaving civilization and heading into the unknown where creatures unlike them have their own private worlds. Some people, like the boy in this excerpt, can be part of this kingdom every day.

There are a great many horses in the high country of the West, and some of them are lucky enough to have a boy to look after them and love them. But there aren't nearly enough boys to go around. That is why Magic, the golden mare, was most particularly lucky to have a boy like Robin Daveen.

It was the greatest kind of luck for both of them, as a matter

of fact, that they had each other, because Magic was not an ordinary horse and Robin was not an ordinary boy.

Magic was a palomino with a mane like fresh pine shavings and a tail to match, and a way of looking out from under her long lashes that made a person think no horse could know so much or like so well the things it saw.

(from *Golden Mare*, by William Corbin)

Would you like to be friends with a horse the way Robin was? Would you like to ride with her into the high country, far from houses and cars, and see another life out of doors?

You will be able to glimpse nature and this animal kingdom in each of the following stories. Even while cars whiz by outside your room, you will be able to enter a silent forest, a dense jungle, or a dark wood and, for a while, leave civilization far behind.

Emily Carr

by Grant Heckman

Emily Carr was a painter from the west coast of Canada who, through her art, helped develop a new way of seeing the wilderness.

As a girl, Emily studied art in California, and later travelled to England to attend school in London. When she returned to Canada, she began to go on sketching trips into the interior of British Columbia. Emily was fascinated by the rough, mountainous countryside, and by the Indians who lived there. Her canvases depict lush forests, totem poles, and Indian villages, all painted with great energy in striking colours.

Like most artists, Emily had to do more than just paint to support herself. She often taught art classes, and especially enjoyed helping children learn how to paint.

In 1910, when she was 39 years old, Emily travelled to France to study painting and was introduced to exciting new styles of painting by French artists. When she returned and showed pictures in her new style, however, people laughed at them and condemned her. After that experience, she hardly painted at all for many year. She earned her living as the landlady of a boarding house, making rugs and pottery, and raising hens, rabbits and dogs for sale.

INDIAN CHURCH, 1929

Emily Carr's studio,
where she lived and worked.

HOUSE FRONT, GOLD HARBOUR,
about 1912

In 1927 she was invited to show some of her paintings in a major exhibit of west coast art presented in Ottawa. While she was in Ontario, Emily met members of the Group of Seven—Canadian artists who were also painting with vivid colours in an unusual, bold way. At that time many people at first found their style disturbing or even ugly, but Emily saw that they were responding to the mystery and power of the scenes they painted, rather than just trying

to reproduce the shapes and colours as in a photograph.

She returned to the west coast excited about painting again, and over the next fifteen years painted the best pictures of her life.

Late in her life, when her health began to fail, Emily began to write books about her childhood, her travels, and her art. When she died at the age of 74 in 1945, Emily Carr was one of Canada's best-known and best-loved artists.

The Truce of the Forest Fire

by Ted Ashlee

We were a motley crew. There was an ash-blond Swede called Whitey, three McMurdo brothers from around Canim Lake way and there was Fergie Ferguson and me. We had been sent out with other gangs of firefighters to a big blaze sixty kilometres east of Prince George. The thermometer had varied from 25 to 30°C for three weeks. The humidity had dropped down to near zero. Then a violent lightning storm had fired the thick pine forest near the mountain top. As usual, the fire had started in an area almost impossible to get at. The heat was so intense that tonnes of water dropped by giant Martin Mars water bombers evaporated before they hit the fire.

The Forestry Department was moving in all its available equipment. There were tank trucks and bulldozers, mattocks and shovels, field telephones and walkie-talkies. Water was carried in our small, hand-operated pumps. Heavy gas-engine powered pumps were lugged along in the hope of finding a creek to supply the water. Most important, there were men. Hundreds of them. Men from the logging camps and the backwoods ranches; small town merchants and tradesmen; greenhorns who had to be watched every second, for if they stepped out of sight of a trail they instantly became lost. There were others, like Fergie Ferguson, who were woodsmen from away back. Such men never panic nor become lost. Fergie was in charge of our outfit and he explained the problem to those with less experience.

"Firefighting calls for teamwork that makes the regular army look like a gang of rookies," he said. "Look at these trees. There's moss growing on them dry as flour. Some call it old man's beard. Here it's Cariboo moss. That catches fire first and then the whole tree burns at once. Here's why. After a dry spell a little glob of pitch forms at the tip of every pine and fir needle. Look at it. It's as easy to light as gasoline."

He was right. We who had fought fires before had seen many a tall pine explode like black gunpowder in one searing flash of flames.

Everything was well organized. Bulldozer operators cut roads through the woods to form fire lines and make some sort of a trail for the water-filled tank trucks to move along. Those in charge of communications set up telephone lines. But mostly we just worked. We felled trees in an attempt to contain the fire. We used up the water in our backpack tanks and slogged back to a tank truck for a refill. Whitey had his hard-hat knocked off by a falling sapling and in the few seconds needed to find it he was struck on the head by a flaming fir limb that burned off half his hair. Stubborn Swede that he was, he refused first aid, jammed his hat on, and went on working. The heat was appalling. Sweat poured down us in rivulets and stung like acid when it ran into cuts and scratches.

We were doing fine. The fire covered over one hundred hectares, we estimated, but it was more or less under control. Then the wind shifted, a high screaming wind out of nowhere. Fergie yelled a warning.

"She's crowning," he shouted. "Everybody out."

A crown fire is completely uncontrollable. Only the tree tops are burning. There is no way to get at them. With such a fire racing before the wind, even water bombers are of little value. The flames jump over the fire guards and falling branches start the forest floor blazing. We ran for it. At the foot of the mountain, we counted noses to see if anyone was missing. Nobody was, so we held a council of war. It was decided that the best plan was to wait until after sundown. The air would be much cooler. The heat rising from the forest fire would cause an updraught. If we were lucky, the updraught would develop into a still breeze and we would start a back fire a few hundred metres downhill from the main fire. Then the whole thing would just burn itself out—if we were lucky. . . .

Everybody cleared out of the area except Fergie's crew. It was our job to keep an eye on things and to order the starting of the back fire when conditions seemed exactly right. But everything went wrong. The back fire was started hours before it should have been. Whether it had been set by someone or by a few wind-driven branches from the crown fire we will never know. There was only one thing to do. Run. Run as hard as we could away from the blazing mountainside towards the back fire. Fergie remembered a pond in a cedar swamp a kilometre away and we headed for it. We just dropped our equipment and pelted down the hill as if the devil were after us.

Well, we made it. In the last stages of exhaustion and with half our clothes burned off our backs we collapsed into the pond and held onto a moss-covered log that reached well out from shore. We pulled handfuls of moss from the log, covered our heads with it and splashed water over each other. Then the animals began to arrive.

We, the fire fighting crew, had often heard about the truce of the forest fire but had never really believed it. It is said that even natural enemies like the deer and the timber wolf run side by side to keep ahead of the flames. Other forest creatures which are normally eaten by predators do the same. The marmots run with the bears and coyotes, the squirrels with the pine martens.

The first to join us was a big mule deer buck, eyes bulging with terror, that cleared our log in one powerful bound and splashed down between Fergie and me. If he'd landed on us, we probably would have been killed. Fergie talked to the buck as if it were a pet dog.

"Take it easy, old timer," he said quietly, patting the animal's nose. Then he noticed that the deer's antlers were hot to the touch, so he covered them with moss and splashed water over them.

By this time, the pond was completely surrounded by fire. The heavy, acrid smoke hung just above the water. We would take a breath and go under for a few seconds. Coming up for air, we would glance around, dodge a few burning branches that fell hissing into the water, and take stock of our animal companions. Deer, coyotes and porcupines were swimming in slow circles. A young she-bear was watching her two small cubs. On a sunken log, a cougar crouched with only its head and flattened ears above water. Only the weasels appeared calm. They floated motionless in the water with their little black noses just showing above the surface.

At nightfall the air cooled a little. We reached up onto our log for fresh moss to protect our heads and found that it was alive with squirrels. There must have been hundreds of them. We were exhausted and the night was endless. It had brought another fear: the danger of falling asleep and drowning. A man could sink unnoticed in the gloom, so we took turns shaking each other awake. Fergie rested with an arm thrown across the mule deer's thick neck. The animal never moved. The fire burned on.

A faint light through the thick smoke told us it was daylight. The fire had died down and we were still alive, but the next problem was how to get out of there.

Walking out of a fire is fully as dangerous as walking into it. Every centimetre of ground is covered with fine white ash. Under it, the glowing red coals may be anything from several centimetres to a metre deep. To step into such a trap is to be instantly barbecued. While we were thinking about it, the she-bear solved the problem for us. Urging her cubs ahead of her, she swam for the west shore. Waist deep in muck and water, and tripping over sunken logs we struggled after her. But the bear knew what she was doing. She came ashore in a creek bed where a shallow trickle of water ran

among the ash-covered boulders. We drank the water, dirty as it was, and were grateful for it.

Too exhausted to estimate time or distance, we just dragged ourselves after the bear. She went her unhurried way, nuzzling the cubs along, often looking over her shoulder to woof a warning about coming too close. Was it hours later? We heard voices. So did the bear. She and her cubs stepped politely to one side and permitted us to pass.

A cheer went up from the firefighters and several rushed to help us. We were red-eyed and bone weary. Most of our clothing had been burned away and our lungs were raw from smoke inhalation.

"We had given you guys up for dead," said one of the men. "You spent the night in a swamp, by the look of you—but how did you get out of that hot ash heap?"

"Nothing to it," Fergie managed a wry grin. "We just followed a bear."

Wild Mouse

by Irene Brady

He fits the description for *Peromyscus leucopus*, the white-footed mouse, in my field guide.

APRIL 6. I've just seen a wild mouse—smooth, sleek, darting across the sinktop. I'm going to try to sketch him.

APRIL 14. I'm trying to win his confidence with cornflakes and apple chunks. If I'm very quiet he stays in sight long enough for me to sketch a little.

APRIL 20. Two weeks of constant coaxing, but it was worth it. He sat and ate sunflower seeds in my hand tonight, but when I moved slightly he was gone ! What a delightful feeling, those tickly toes on my palm!

APRIL 30. He's getting so tubby I can't believe it! Maybe I should stop feeding him, but he's so beautiful to watch (even though he is fat). . . . He's building a nest someplace. He's made a total wreck of the toilet paper roll.

When he's nervous he hugs the floor.

MAY 5. He is a she! I pulled out the drawer of the coffee mill because I heard scratching inside and I'm watching a small miracle. She chewed a hole in the back of the mill, built a snug nest, and is crouched in its hollow having babies. One tiny red thing lies beside her and another seems to be coming. The mother is ignoring me. She's busy.

The baby is tiny—maybe only an inch and a half long. It just crawled clumsily under its mother—maybe to nurse? It's 1:08 p.m.

1:16 p.m. Eight minutes later . . . the second baby has been born now, with the mother mouse watching very closely and licking it thoroughly.

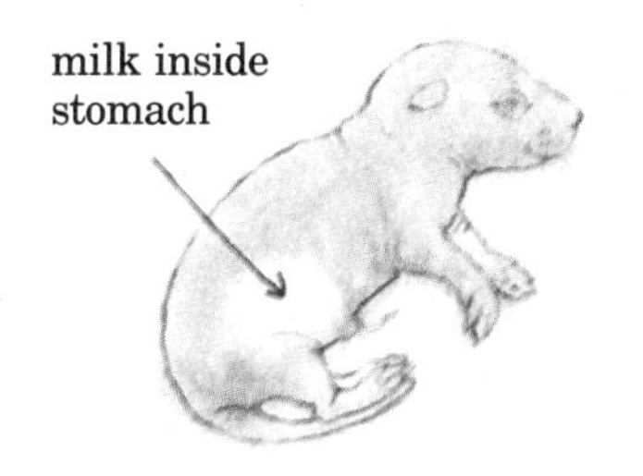

Now she's bitten the umbilical cord through and is eating the afterbirth. It looks like a disk with a rolled edge. I guess the rolled edge is what rolled back off the baby—like peeling a sock off a foot. . . . Just got a look at the first baby again. Its skin is transparent. I can see the white milk in its stomach and dark pupils through its eyelids!

1:30 p.m. The third baby just popped out tail-first, really fast, and the mother is licking him. Who'd ever guess these ugly, salmon-pink things could grow up to be beautiful wild mice?

1:38 p.m. It only took the third baby eight minutes to get to its mother's milk. They're all nursing now—legs beating and kneading in rhythm with their sucking. Their ears are just lumps. The tips seem to be fastened down over the openings. They have tiny whiskers and eyebrows. Their toes are stuck together except at the very tips.

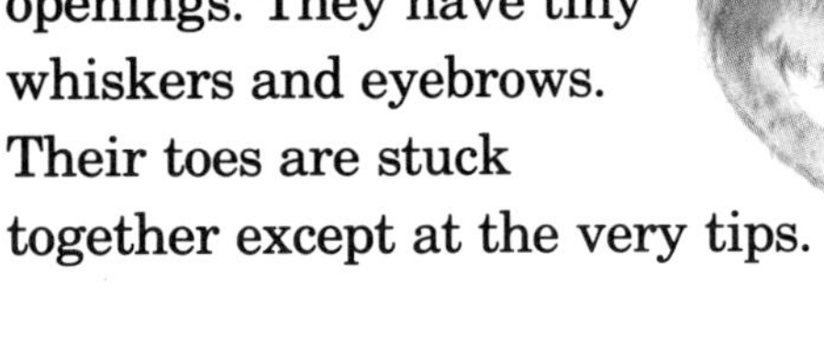

(I had to quit sketching. The mother mouse woke up and got very distressed when she saw me. More tomorrow, I hope.)

MAY 7. Two days old. Their skins are so loose they flop. Mother is gone, so it won't bother her if I sketch. One baby is scratching its head with a hind foot but can't keep upright. No co-ordination. They're so lively. They look like they're made of red rubber. I can see the blood vessels in their feet when I hold them to the light. The babies are still hairless except for eyebrows and whiskers.

Scratching is hard work!

This one was washing its face.

MAY 9. Four days old. Their ears have come unstuck! They're starting to groom themselves. They try to sit up but keep falling over. The front toes are separated but not the back toes. The babies are moving around in the nest a lot.

Colour is starting to show. Brown hairs
are sprouting on their upper parts
and white hairs on the undersides.

May 10. Five days old.
They're getting fat but still don't
fill up those loose skins. My sketching
visits disturb the mother so I do it when
she's gone. Sometimes when she leaves the nest she
drags a baby out attached to her teats—they really hang
on tight! She carries them in when she notices.

May 12. One week old. I can see their two-tone colouring
clearly now. Their skin is nearly covered by fur. They're chubby.
They've filled those loose skins and the coffee mill, too.

They're about three inches from nose to tail tip. I've just noticed
something about their ears—although the tips came unstuck
when they were four days old, the ears are
still sealed inside. I wonder how well
(or even if) the baby mice can hear . . .

These two fell asleep in my hand.

MAY 16. She moved them. It took me a few days to track them down. They're eleven days old now and she's having trouble keeping them in the hole in the old chair cushion she's using as a nest.

They're active and wiggly, beautiful wild mouselings with fat tails and sleek coats. Still blind. Ears are opened now!

They're about four inches long.

They're beginning to use their tails for balance—beforc, the tail just dragged along behind. Now it whips and counterweights as the baby creeps and explores.

MAY 19. Two weeks old. Four bright eyes gazed at me in astonishment today when I lifted up the loose cotton from the top of the nest. The third mouseling is still in its blind baby-world, but these two are on the brink of growing up. Now that they can see, they're afraid of me. They jump like crickets at a sudden movement or sharp noise.

MAY 21. Sixteen days old. I saw a movement from the corner of my eye as I sat reading . . .

. . . and there was the mother mouse leading a skittery line of babies toward the cupboard where the oatmeal stays. I always leave an open box of it on the shelf for her. Now she's teaching the little ones to forage.

They still nurse, but altogether they weigh more than she does. They look like miniature adults with tiny ears and too-short tails.

When they all nurse at once they lift her right off the ground.

MAY 31. The little family has left its nest. Mama seems to be getting "tubby" again. Under the table two bright black eyes twinkle up at me, crunching sounds come from the oatmeal cupboard, and there is a whisper of tiny feet from the attic—these things tell me my wild mouse family has grown up.

Orange Kitten

Small orange kitten
Caught crying in the tree
All among the autumn leaves
Orange and red and brown
Is like a small leaf
That wants to come down.

Charm for a Sick Dog

Dear Dog,
Get well,
Wound heal,
Fur grow,
Spirit rise,
Stomach settle,
Grow strong,
Stay well.

But I See Sparrows!

This morning I saw
circling and circling,
A small brown sparrow
Outside my window.

Rising and falling
It soared in the wind
Then gently fluttered
To the ground.

I looked again
And saw a dry leaf
Given wings for a moment
To fly in the sun.

Some will always see leaves
On the ground,
But I see sparrows
Waiting for wind.

I Sing to the Stars

I sing to the stones and the sea and the sky,
I sing to the lost ones, the child I hear cry.
I sing to the smokestacks, subways and streetcars,
And when it is night, I sing to the stars.

Poems by Nancy Prasad

from

THE MIDNIGHT FOX

by Betsy Byars

I had no intention of going to sleep when I lay down on the bed; I did not think I would ever be able to sleep again, but that is what I did. I fell right asleep and did not even move until four hours later when I awoke. It was one o'clock in the morning.

The storm was in full force, or perhaps it was a second storm, but the house was quiet. I got up and went out into the hall. I could not hear anything but the sound of the rain and Hazeline's transistor radio, which was sputtering with static beside her on the pillow.

I went down the stairs, one by one. I did not make a sound. I stepped on the part of the steps near the wall because Petie had told me that was how burglars got up stairs unheard. I was just stepping into the hall when, without warning, the hall light went on. Aunt Millie was standing there in her bathrobe squinting at me.

"What's wrong?" she asked.

"Nothing. I just didn't know what time it was."

"Well—" she looked closely at her watch "—it's just past one o'clock."

"I went to sleep in my clothes."

"Well, you get on your pajamas and get back to bed. This is the first good sleeping night we've had, and you mustn't let it go to waste."

"Sure."

"Well, go on back up the steps." She watched me go up two steps and then she said,

"Goodness, we've gotten on so well all summer, I'd hate for anything to happen now right before your parents get home."

"Aunt Millie, did Uncle Fred get the fox?"

"No."

"Is he still out on the porch?"

"In this rain? No, he is fast asleep in his bed like you ought to be."

She waited until I was up the stairs and then she turned out the light. I went into my room and she called, "Are you getting in bed?"

I lay down. "Yes."

"And go to sleep."

I lay in bed for a long time, still in my clothes, and then I got up very carefully. I walked over to the window and looked out at the tree. I opened the window, pushed out the screen, reached out into the rain, and felt for the smooth spot Aunt Millie had told me was worn into the bark of the tree.

I took off my shoes and knelt on the window sill. There was an enormous flash of lightning that turned the whole world white for a moment, and then I climbed out onto the nearest branch and circled the trunk round with my arms.

I thought that I could never get one step farther. I thought that I could never move even one muscle or I would fall. I thought that in the morning when Aunt Millie came up to see why I wasn't at breakfast she would find me here, pressed into the tree, still frozen with fear.

The rain was hard and slanting directly into my face. Finally I got up just enough courage to turn my face out of the rain. Then the lightning flashed again and I saw the ground about a million metres below. I held the tree so tightly the bark was cutting into my cheek.

I don't know how long I stayed that way. If I had tried to look at my watch, just that little movement would have thrown me off balance. After a while, though, I began to sort of slip down the tree. I never let go of the main trunk for a second. I just moved my arms downward in very small movements. Then, slowly, when I was practically kneeling on the first limb, I let my foot reach down for the next one.

If there were smooth spots on those branches, my feet never found them. They only touched one rough limb after another as, slowly, I kept inching down the tree, feeling my way, never looking down at the ground until, finally, my foot reached out for another limb and felt the cold wet grass. It shocked me for a moment and

then I jumped down, landing on my hands and knees.

I got up and ran to the rabbit hutch. The baby fox was huddled in one corner of the pen where there was some shelter from the rain. The lightning flashed and I saw him watching me.

"I'm going to get you out," I said.

He crouched back farther in the hutch. In the next flash of lightning, I looked on the ground for a rock and I saw at my feet a small dead frog. I knew that the black fox in all this rain had brought that frog here to her baby. She was right now watching me somewhere.

There were bricks stacked in a neat pile under the hutch, and I took one and began to bang it against the lock. I was prepared to do this all night if necessary, but the lock was an old one and it opened right away.

The noise had scared the baby fox and he was now making a whimpering sound. I unhooked the broken lock, opened the cage, and stepped back against the tree.

The baby fox did not move for a moment. I could barely see him, a small dark ball in the back of the cage. He waited, alert and suspicious, and then, after a moment he moved in a crouch to the door of the cage. He cried sharply. From the bushes there was an answering bark.

He crouched lower. The lightning flashed again and in that second he jumped and ran in the direction of the bushes. He barked as he ran. There was an immediate answer, and then only the sound of the rain. I waited against the tree, thinking about them, and then I heard the black fox bark one more time as she ran through the orchard with her baby.

And I thought, someday I will be in a famous museum, walking along on the marble floors, looking at paintings. There will be one called "Blue Flowers" and I will look at that for a while, and the next one will be "Woman on the Beach" and I will look at that for a while, and then I will glance at the name of the next painting and it will be "Fox with Baby at Midnight," and I will look up and my heart will stop beating because there it will be, just the way it was this night, the black fox and her baby running beneath the wet ghostly apple trees toward a patch of light in the distance. And I thought, leaning against that tree in the rain, if there is a picture like that, I hope sometime I will get to see it.

Suddenly the rain began to slacken and I walked around the house. I had never been so wet in my life and now that it was over, I was cold too. And I was tired. I looked up at the tree and there didn't seem to be any point in climbing back up when in just a few hours everyone would know what I had done anyway. I went up on the porch and rang the doorbell.

from

A Place for Margaret

by Bernice Thurman Hunter

The first time we met he bit me. I held out my hand, straight and flat, just like Aunt Margaret said, but Starr snapped at it so excitedly with his big yellow teeth that he nipped my skin and made it bleed. It hurt like the dickens and I yelled blue murder, scaring the wits out of him. Then he turned tail and galloped across the meadow, disappearing into the woods on the other side.

The next time was just as bad. I was lying in the hammock feeling sorry for myself and missing the city noises. I wasn't used to the quiet of the country, where all you ever heard were bees and bugs and the odd cow mooing. My home in Toronto was on Jones

Avenue right near Gerrard Street, where the air practically vibrated with the clanging of trolley cars, the squealing of sirens and the racket of a hundred screaming kids.

So at first I spent a lot of my time on the farm lying around pining for home. I did this in the hammock that Uncle Herb had slung between two poles in the front yard especially for me. There were lots of trees he could have slung it from but Aunt Marg said I wouldn't get enough sunshine under them. "Of all God's miracles," she said, and she could name them off by the peck, "sunshine is far and away the best. It cures nearly anything that ails you." Anything except loneliness, I thought dejectedly.

That day, as I was lazing in the sun talking to my imaginary friend, Emily (I had invented Emily so I wouldn't go crazy), I suddenly had this creepy feeling come over me that somebody was watching me. I swivelled my eyes around nervously, and there was Starr with his big brown head lolling over the fence staring straight at me.

We eyed each other curiously. I don't know what he thought of me, but I thought he was beautiful. He was chestnut brown with a white star the length of his nose, a thick tawny mane and the most peculiar long white eyelashes I'd ever seen on a horse. He batted them at me now, sweeping them down over his shiny dark eyes, which just happened to be the same colour as my own.

I got out of the hammock the quickest way I knew how, by rolling over and landing kerplunk on the ground. Startled, he flung up his head, gave a piercing whinny and went tearing across the field as if the devil himself were after him.

"What did you do to him?" called Aunt Marg from the porch. She set down the two pails of milk she was carrying and threw her floppy straw hat up on a nail.

"Nothing!" I pouted, close to tears. "He just doesn't like me, I guess."

"Well, never you mind," she laughed, holding the door open with her backside and lifting the pails into the kitchen. "I like you!" The door clacked shut behind her.

I already knew that! But I wanted Starr to like me. So the next time he hung his head over the fence I was ready for him. Instead of being in the hammock, I was sitting stock-still on the little bench that I had dragged down from the porch—the one Aunt Marg set her bread tins out on. Rising slowly to my feet, I tiptoed towards him, carefully balancing two sugar cubes on the end of a long, flat stick. But as soon as I got close to him he bolted.

"Dang!" I swore, throwing the stick at the fence. "Not even a *horse* will come near me!"

Boy, I was lonely those first weeks on Uncle Herb's farm. Every night I'd say to Aunt Margaret, "I want to go home." And she'd say, "But Margaret"—I was named after her—"if you go home the doctor will send you to the TB sanitarium. You don't want that, now do you?" And I'd say, "No, but at least at the sanitarium there might be other sick kids to play with."

That's why I had been sent to the farm. Because the doctor said I had TB, which is short for tuberculosis, and I had to be isolated. "It's either the san or the farm," he said, "take your pick." So my mother picked the farm.

In that summer of 1925, sunshine, home-cooking and good nursing care were all that could be done for TB. My mother said I was bound to get plenty of all three on the farm. "My sister Margaret is the best practical nurse in Ontario. Maybe in the whole country," she declared proudly. "Why, she's nursed hundreds of sick folk back to health after the doctors had given them up for lost. And she's only buried half a dozen so far."

"How long will I be gone, Ma?" I was beginning to get suspicious. What if I was dying and they weren't telling me?

"Oh, just a few weeks at the most, Peg." That's what I got called at home—Peg or Peggy. I didn't like either one. "Don't worry your head. Margaret will have you fit as a fiddle in no time at all."

Next came the problem of how to get me there. The farm was sixty odd miles from Toronto, and my father didn't own a car. And I was too weak to travel by train. So the doctor volunteered to deliver me himself. He said his folks lived in Shelburne, which was the nearest town to Uncle Herb's farm, and he owed them a visit.

So Ma packed my grip and slipped a snapshot of our whole family into the side pocket. "Just so you don't forget us," she said.

Then the doctor bundled me in a woollen rug and laid me out on the back seat of his Pierce Arrow. It had a lovely new-car smell and I would have enjoyed the trip if I'd been feeling better. On the other hand, if I'd been feeling better I wouldn't have got to go. So it was six of one and half a dozen of the other.

Curled up on the velvety seat, I soon fell fast asleep. The next thing I knew the doctor was calling, "Wake up, missy. We're here!"

I jumped up, rubbing my eyes, and stared out the front window as he steered the Arrow up the long lane leading to the green farmhouse. At least it used to be green, but now the paint was flaking off, letting the parched grey wood show through. A weather-beaten sign nailed to the fencepost read, in faded letters, *Green Meadows*.

My aunt and uncle were both on the porch to greet us. Uncle Herb was a solid looking man, with wiry red hair, a friendly grin that showed the space between his teeth, and a farmer's burnt complexion. He had on grey overalls and a blue-checkered shirt. Aunt Marg was a stockily built woman in a house-dress that looked as if it had been cut from the same cloth as Uncle Herb's shirt. She had red hair coiled up in a bun, fair freckly skin and a wide sweet smile. They looked almost like twins.

The first thing I said was, "Am I going to die?"

Uncle Herb let out a hoot of laughter and the straw he had been wiggling between his teeth flew out of his mouth. "You do and your aunt will kill you!" he cried.

That made us all laugh. Then the doctor assured me that I was going to get well, and my aunt and uncle thanked him for dropping me off (like a sack of potatoes, joked Uncle Herb). I was soon tucked in under an afghan on the day bed in the big farm kitchen.

I liked the kitchen. It was a homey room with a huge black iron stove, a long wooden table and six plain chairs. A washstand stood by the door with a graniteware basin on top and a pail of water

underneath. The floor was made of wide boards with no linoleum. At the end of the room was a door that led upstairs to the bedrooms.

Both my aunt and uncle were nice, which in my experience is pretty unusual. Most often if your aunt is nice your uncle is awful—or vice versa.

Aunt Marg worried a lot about my loneliness because she said that pining would hinder my progress. But since I wasn't allowed within a mile of other people, especially children, what could she do?

Of course she spent as much time with me as she could spare. Every night before bed she'd play a game of dominoes with me or read me a story when the TB made me too tired to read to myself.

But because it was the haying season and Uncle Herb didn't have a hired hand, Aunt Marg had to help out. So she had to leave me on my own more than she really liked.

It was a small farm, with just one horse—Starr, two cows—Flora and Fauna, and a flock of black and white hens that Aunt Marg called her "ladies." They didn't have regular names like the other livestock. Uncle Herb said his farm was a one-man operation.

"One man and one woman!" Aunt Marg reminded him dryly.

"You're right there, Mag." That's what he called her sometimes—Mag. She didn't like it because it rhymed with hag, but there was no use trying to stop him. "That man!" she wagged her finger in his direction. "That uncle of yours. Why, if I didn't love him so much I'd have sent him packing long ago!"

The second week I was there it rained cats and dogs so I had to stay indoors and rest on the day bed, with only my imaginary friend, Emily, for company. Sometimes I heard Starr neighing in the distance, which only made me feel more lonely.

Then one day Uncle Herb came in sopping wet; he slapped his hat on his knee and showered me with raindrops as he handed me a letter. I recognized the writing instantly. It was from my sister Josie, the one I was the closest to and shared the bed with at home. Squealing with delight, I ripped it open.

June 16, 1925.

Dear Peg,

How are you? I hope you are lots better. We're all fine down here. We are having a swell summer so far. Do you know what we did last Saturday? We had a block picnic and all the families on our block went to High Park. All the mothers packed lunch baskets. Ma made egg and balogna sandwiches and gumdrop cake.

There must have been a hundred people there altogether. Even Olive and Elmer went. (Olive and Elmer were the oldest in our family and they usually thought they were too grown-up to go on family outings.) The minute we jumped off the trolley car we all trooped down to where the animals are kept and fed them carrot tops through the fence. Then we played games like Shadow Tag and Cowboys and Indians. That's lots of fun in High Park because there are so many big trees to hide behind. The big boys played Buck, Buck, How Many Fingers Up? Our Harry was at the bottom of the heap and he nearly got his back broke when fat Theodore Duncan landed on top of him. So Jenny begged him to quit. (Jenny was Harry's twin so they were extra close.) Gracie and Davey were good as gold and didn't fight once because they were having so much fun playing London Bridges and Here I Sit A-Sewing. Bobby wet his drawers once so Ma put him back in napkins, but she didn't spank him. Flossie Gilmore went with Zelma Speares because Mrs. Gilmore had the vapours and couldn't go. (Flossie Gilmore was my best friend, but who the heck was Zelma Speares?)

At suppertime the men put the picnic tables in rows, end to end, so we could all sit down together. There was tons of food and oceans of lemonade. Afterwards we kids layed around on the grass moaning and holding our stomachs. Then we started telling jokes and stories.

When the women got the tables all cleared up and the men came back from their walk, the grownups played progressive euchre. The big kids, like Olive and Elmer, were allowed to play too.

On our way home on the trolley car we flipped the wicker seatbacks over so we could ride facing each other. Then everybody sang "Hail, hail, the gang's all here, what the heck do we care, long as we got our carfare" and after that we sang "Show me the way to go home, over land or sea or foam." It was the most fun I ever had in my life. Even better than kids' day at the Ex and rides at Sunnyside. Too bad you missed it.

I was so tired when I got home I went to bed without washing myself and Ma didn't even notice. I really like sleeping alone. There's no one to poke me when I wiggle my toes, and make me shove over. And it doesn't matter that the bed sinks down in the middle when there's only one person in it. But I miss you quite a bit, Peg, and hope you miss me too. Goodbye. Write soon.

Your sister, Josie.

P.S. Ma and Pa want to add a line.

Hello there, daughter. I hope you're being a good girl and not giving any trouble. And I hope this finds you well. Write me a note when you feel up to it. I'll hand the pen to your Pa now.

Your loving mother.

Well, Peg, we received your aunt's welcome letter a day or two ago saying how much better you are. That's sure good news to us. We'll be looking for you home at the end of the summer.

Lovingly, your father.

That night I went to bed early, but I didn't blow out the lamp right away. Instead, I got the picture of my family down off the washstand mirror and studied it for a long time. We all looked so happy standing in a bunch on the steps of our house on Jones Avenue. I noticed every little thing—the welcome mat hanging crooked over the railing, Bobby's damp drawers drooping down, our old Flyer wagon lying on its side on the weedy lawn. I remembered what fun it was coasting down the hill on Jones Avenue. I stared hard at each face, especially Ma's and Pa's, hoping I could make myself dream about them.

I sighed and stuck the snapshot back up on the looking glass. Then I spread-eagled myself on the bed. It *was* nice having a bed to myself. And my own room, too! At home there were two beds in each room and two kids to a bed. My bed on the farm was a double one that didn't sink in the middle. And it was extra soft because it had a downy feather tick. And Emily never wiggled her toes and she didn't take up any space at all.

Now, if only I could win over that stubborn horse!

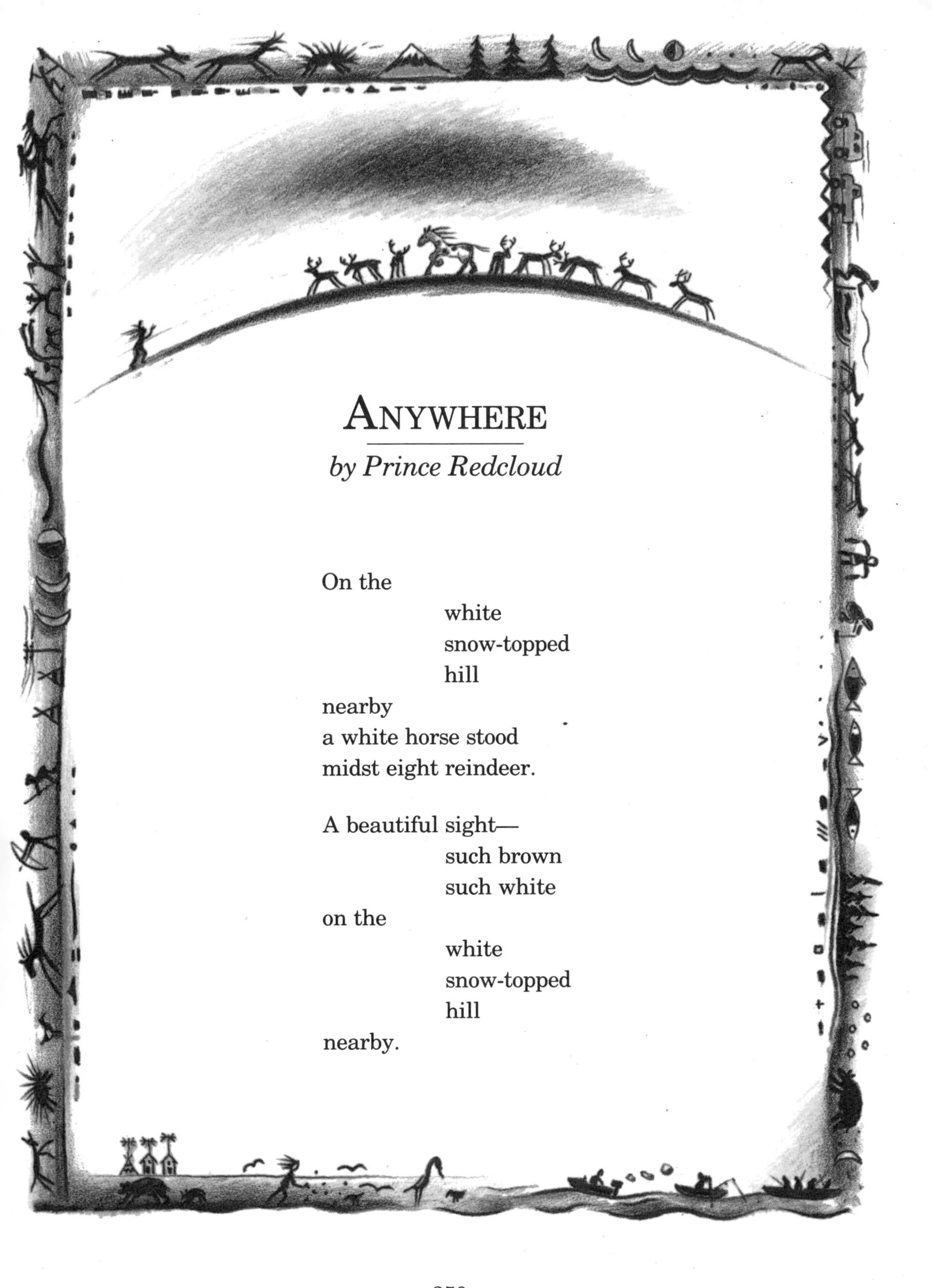

ANYWHERE

by Prince Redcloud

On the
                    white
                    snow-topped
                    hill
nearby
a white horse stood
midst eight reindeer.

A beautiful sight—
                    such brown
                    such white
on the
                    white
                    snow-topped
                    hill
nearby.

Wild Horses

by Ron Watts

from Owl Magazine

Diary of an RCMP Horse Trainer

as told to Barbara Chernin

The scarlet-coated Royal Canadian Mounted Police and their jet-black horses perform a spectacular program of formation riding set to music. The Musical Ride dazzles crowds around the world. But where does the road to stardom begin?

June 22 After two years as a rider in the Musical Ride, here I am, waiting to train my first horse. I've been assigned a filly named Dancer, one of the new three-year-olds just arrived from the ranch. She's kind of skinny, and I don't like the way she lays back her ears every time I go near her.

Aug 10 I've never seen a horse buck as hard as Dancer does at the mere touch of the blanket to her back. I've got to stop her bucking by the end of September, or it's back to the ranch for Dancer.

Sept 14 I checked out a noise in the stable last night. The door to the oat room was wide open— oats all over—and Dancer wasn't in her stall. I found her behind Dominic's stall chewing the last of her

stolen midnight snack. She's a smart horse all right, so why won't she take a saddle? Maybe it's my fault—every other trainer's on schedule but me!

Sept 28 Dancer still bucks every time I try to saddle her up. What am I doing wrong?

Oct 3 We did it! Dancer finally allowed me to put a saddle on her back. I tried a little bit of smooth talk and some friendly pats on the neck—and it worked! Why didn't I think of that before? Guess I've still got a lot to learn...

Nov 10 Been riding Dancer for three days--and no bucking. She understands every verbal command I give her and lets me know when she thinks she deserves a pat. How could I have wanted to send her back to the ranch?

Dec 15 Today, I was walking Dancer on a lunge line to help even her stride. Suddenly a trapdoor on the catwalk above us slammed shut. I jumped sky-high, but Dancer only backed up slightly and then calmly finished her circuit. Looks as if Dancer has the personality of a true Musical Ride horse—unflappable.

Jan 23 At last we're getting down to the real thing—preparation exercises for the Musical Ride. Dancer's walking and trotting beautifully, and moves from a slow trot to a fast canter with ease. The Head Trainer says Dancer's coming along well, and I'm proud of her.

April 20 Dancer's really grown—I can hardly believe how strong and beautiful she is. And smart! Today Dominic nipped her during dressage. Dancer flinched, but didn't break her stride. She simply waited until Dominic passed by her again, then delivered a well-aimed kick to his rear end. We all had a good laugh.

July 10 Dancer's over at the ranch for summer vacation—I'm still here working with some new horses. Think I'll take Dancer some apples and see how she's doing.

Jan 5 It's nearly two years since I started training Dancer. Now she understands the slightest leg pressure or pull of the reins, and I don't even bother with verbal commands anymore. She's breezing through a new set of dressage exercises like a real pro. The kids who come to visit the stables really like her too! Who would have thought that scrawny little filly who came into my life two years ago would have turned out so well?

One Year (of hard work) Later! Dancer's working hard in the final stage of training. She's so good, sometimes I think she's reading my mind. We're rehearsing to see which horses will make it into the "Lead File". All 32 horses in the Musical Ride are special, but only four will be chosen to head up the ranks. Dancer reverses and side-steps with the best of them, and stays in formation most of the time.

Jan 10 Dancer made Lead File today! Her rider is Constable Morgan. I've heard good things about Morgan—bet she and Dancer will make a fantastic team. I'll be watching. You know, I miss Dancer already.

June 18 Can hardly believe I've been keeping this diary for three years now. Dancer's on her way to Osaka, Japan with the Musical Ride. Today the Head Trainer assigned me a new three-year-old named Fireball. His tail droops, he steps on my feet, and I'm not too crazy about the look in his eye. But we'll see, miracles do happen...

from

The Ghost Horse of the Mounties

by sean o huigin

imagine if you will the empty plains
imagine if you will a sultry summer night
imagine if you will a brilliant edge
of gold on the horizon
and a silence getting deeper all the time

listen now
the time is long ago
listen close and let yourself go back
imagine if you can that you're a young man
standing in the prairie grass
alone

it's summer's june
a june of heat and silence now
it's summer's june
in 1874

the northwest territories then
it's manitoba canada right now
a little place called dufferin
those days
and gathered there a group of men
who someday would be famous
round the world

listen now
there is no wind to hear
look again and see horizon's gold
a golden line made by the setting sun
a line that moves and changes as you
watch

look up and see the evening sky
dark blue
a clearness in the air you almost
feel
behind you
to the east horizon's dark
an almost black that changes as
you turn
to that dark blue above then lighter
down to that fine line of fiery gold

imagine if you can
you're a young man
standing in the prairie grass
alone
a little distance over a small rise
a group of wagons
tents and men
are formed

and most of all
a little way beyond
two hundred fifty horses
lift their heads

their ears prick up
they wave them back and forth
their nostrils flare as each one
smells the air

now try
try hard
imagine now with all the
might you have
imagine that a certain horse
is you

a slim black horse
with muscles strong and
hard
a white maned horse
long silky tail to match

you're standing in the long
tall prairie grass
you've travelled many miles
from the east
you rode on trains
you carried men
you pulled the wagons
and tonight you rest

tonight
you rest
but why then is a
restlessness amongst you and
your friends
why does the empty sky
give no delight

together now you sniff
the air again
what is it that you seem
to smell that scares
together now you listen
to no sounds
you twitch your tail
you shake your mane
and all the other horses
stamp their feet

imagine now
and find a special name
a horse's name that will
be yours alone
a magic name that's faster
than a shooting star
and brighter than the
full white moon at night

imagine now
imagine that young man
who's standing in the prairie grass
alone
for he's the man who rides you in
the day
and he's the man who combs your
mane at night

and listen now
what is it that you hear
a whispering of words from
over there
the sound the young man's thinking
in your head
that special wind that blows
from you to him
and back
and carries in between
the thoughts you think
and no one else
can hear

you feel together
something strange
a much too stillness
settling on the night
you feel the cold
the shivers running
up and down the
other's spine
you feel the fear
that comes
for while the night
is still and hot
it creeps inside
your souls and
leaves a chill

from

The Black Stallion

by Walter Farley

The tramp steamer *Drake* ploughed away from the coast of India and pushed its blunt prow into the Arabian Sea, homeward bound. Slowly it made its way west toward the Gulf of Aden. Its hold was loaded with coffee, rice, tea, oil seeds and jute. Black smoke poured from its one stack, darkening the hot cloudless sky.

Alexander Ramsay, known to his friends back home in New York City as Alec, leaned over the rail and watched the water slide away from the sides of the boat. His red hair blazed redder than ever in the hot sun; his tanned elbows rested heavily on the rail as he turned his freckled face back toward the fast-disappearing shore.

It had been fun—those two months in India. He would miss Uncle Ralph, miss the days they had spent together in the jungle, even the screams of the panthers and the many eerie sounds of the jungle night. Never again would he think of a missionary's work as easy work. No, sir, you had to be big and strong, able to ride horseback for long hours through the tangled jungle paths. Alec glanced down proudly at the hard muscles in his arms. Uncle Ralph had taught him how to ride—the one thing in the world he had always wanted to do.

But it was all over now. Rides back home would be few.

His fist opened. Lovingly he surveyed the pearl pocketknife he held there. The inscription on it was in gold: *To Alec on his birthday, Bombay, India.* He remembered, too, his uncle's words: "A knife, Alec, comes in handy sometimes."

Suddenly a large hand descended on his shoulder. "Well, m'boy, you're on your way home," a gruff voice said, with a decidedly English accent.

Alec looked up into the captain's wrinkled, wind-tanned face. "Hello, Captain Watson," he answered. "It's rather a long way home, though, sir. To England with you and then to New York on the *Majestic.*"

"And you're going home alone?"

"Yes, sir! School opens next month and I have to be there."

The captain smiled and took Alec by the arm. "Come along," he said, "I'll show you how we steer this ship and what makes it go."

The *Drake* kept near the coast of Arabia—endless miles of barren desert shore. But Alec's thoughts were not on the scorching sand. Arabia—where the greatest horses in the world were bred! Did other fellows dream of horses the way he did? To him, a horse was the greatest animal in the world.

Then one day the *Drake* headed for a small Arabian port. As they approached the small landing, Alec saw a crowd of Arabs milling about in great excitement. Obviously it was not often that a boat stopped there.

But, as the gangplank went down with a bang, Alec could see that it wasn't the ship itself that was attracting all the attention. The Arabs were crowding toward the centre of the landing. Alec heard a whistle—shrill, loud, clear, unlike anything he had ever heard before. He saw a mighty black horse rear on its hind legs, its forelegs striking out into the air. A white scarf was tied across its eyes. The crowd broke and ran.

White lather ran from the horse's body; his mouth was open, his teeth bared. He was a giant of a horse, glistening black—too big to be pure Arabian. His mane was like a crest, mounting, then falling low. His neck was long and slender, and arched to the small, savagely beautiful head. The head was that of the wildest of all wild creatures—a stallion born wild—and it was beautiful, savage, splendid. A stallion with a wonderful physical perfection that matched his savage, ruthless spirit.

Once again the Black screamed and rose on his hind legs. Alec could hardly believe his eyes and ears—a stallion, a wild stallion—unbroken, such as he had read and dreamed about!

Two ropes led from the halter on the horse's head, and four men were attempting to pull the stallion toward the gangplank. They were going to put him on the ship! Alec saw a dark-skinned man, wearing European dress and a high, white turban, giving directions. In his hand he held a whip. He gave his orders tersely in Arabic. Suddenly he walked to the rear of the horse and let the hard whip fall on the Black's hindquarters. The stallion bolted so fast that he struck one of the Arabs holding the rope; down the man went and lay still. The Black snorted and plunged; if ever Alec saw hate expressed by a horse, he saw it then. They had him halfway up the plank. Alec wondered where they would put him if they ever did succeed in getting him on the boat.

Then he was on! Alec saw Captain Watson waving his arms frantically, motioning and shouting for the men to pull the stallion toward the stern. The boy followed at a safe distance. Now he saw the makeshift stall into which they were attempting to get the Black—it had once been a good-sized cabin. The *Drake* had little accommodation for transporting animals; its hold was already heavily laden with cargo.

The days that followed were hectic ones for Alec, passengers and crew. He had never dreamed a horse could have such spirit, be so untamable. The ship resounded far into the night from the blows struck by those powerful legs. The outside of the stall was now covered with reinforcements. The dark-skinned man became more

mysterious than ever—always alone, and never talking to anyone but the captain.

Every night Alec would steal up to the stall, leave some lumps of sugar he had taken from the dinner table, and depart; sometimes he would see the Black and other times he would only hear the ring of hoofs against the floor.

The *Drake* stopped at Alexandria, Bengasi, Tripoli, Tunis and Algiers, passed the Rock of Gibraltar and turned north up the coast of Portugal. Now they were off Cape Finisterre on the coast of Spain, and in a few days, Captain Watson told Alec, they would be in England.

Alec wondered why the Black was being shipped to England—perhaps for stud, perhaps to race. The slanting shoulders, the deep broad chest, the powerful legs, the knees not too high nor too low—these, his uncle had taught him, were marks of speed and endurance.

That night Alec made his customary trip to the stall, his pockets filled with lumps of sugar. The night was hot and still; heavy clouds blacked out the stars; in the distance long streaks of lightning raced through the sky. The Black had his head out the window. He was looking out to sea, his nostrils quivering more than ever. He turned, whistled as he saw the boy, then again faced the water.

Alec felt elated—it was the first time that the stallion hadn't drawn back into the stall at sight of him. He moved closer. He put the sugar in the palm of his hand and hesitantly held it out to the stallion. The Black turned and once again whistled—softer this time. Alec stood his ground. Neither he nor anyone else had been this close to the stallion since he came on board. But he did not care to take the chance of extending his arm any nearer the bared teeth, the curled nostrils. Instead he placed the sugar on the sill. The Black looked at it, then back at the boy. Slowly he moved over and began to eat the sugar. Alec watched him for a moment, satisfied; then as the rain began to fall, he went back to his cabin.

He was awakened with amazing suddenness in the middle of the night. The *Drake* lurched crazily and he was thrown onto the

floor. Outside there were loud rolls of thunder, and streaks of lightning made his cabin as light as day.

His first storm at sea! He pushed the light switch—it was dead. Then a flash of lightning again illuminated the cabin. The top of his bureau had been swept clear and the floor was covered with broken glass. Hurriedly he pulled on his pants and shirt and started for the door; then he stopped. Back he went to the bed, fell on his knees and reached under. He withdrew a life jacket and strapped it around him. He hoped that he wouldn't need it.

He opened the door and made his way, staggering, to the deck. The fury of the storm drove him back into the passageway; he hung on to the stair rail and peered into the black void. He heard the shouts of Captain Watson and the crew faintly above the roar of the winds. Huge waves swept from one end of the *Drake* to the other. Hysterical passengers crowded into the corridor. Alec was genuinely scared now; never had he seen a storm like this!

For what seemed hours, the *Drake* ploughed through wave after wave, trembling, careening on its side, yet somehow managing to stay afloat. The long streaks of lightning never diminished; zigzagging through the sky, their sharp cracks resounded on the water.

From the passageway, Alec saw one of the crew make his way along the deck in his direction, desperately fighting to hold on to the rail. The *Drake* rolled sideways and a huge wave swept over the boat. When it had passed, the sailor was gone. The boy closed his eyes and prayed.

The storm began to subside a little and Alec felt new hope. Then suddenly a bolt of fire seemed to fall from the heavens above them. A sharp crack and the boat shook. Alec was thrown flat on his face, stunned. Slowly he regained consciousness. He was lying on his stomach; his face felt hot and sticky. He raised his hand, and withdrew it covered with blood. Then he became conscious of feet stepping on him. The passengers, yelling and screaming, were climbing, crawling over him! The *Drake* was still—its engines dead.

Struggling, Alec pushed himself to his feet. Slowly he made his way along the deck. His startled eyes took in the scene about him. The *Drake*, struck by lightning, seemed almost cut in half! They were sinking! Strange, with what seemed the end so near, he should feel so calm. They were manning the lifeboats, and Captain Watson was there shouting directions. One boat was being lowered into the water. A large wave caught it broadside and turned it over—its occupants disappeared in the sea.

The second lifeboat was being filled and Alec waited his turn. But when it came, the boat had reached its quota.

"Wait for the next one, Alec," Captain Watson said sternly. He put his arm on the boy's shoulder, softening the harshness of his words.

As they watched the second lifeboat being lowered, the dark-skinned man appeared and rushed up to the captain, waving his arms and babbling hysterically.

"It's under the bed, under the bed!" Captain Watson shouted at him.

Then Alec saw the man had no life jacket. Terror in his eyes, he turned away from the captain toward Alec. Frantically he rushed at the boy and tried to tear the life jacket from his back. Alec struggled, but he was no match for the half-crazed man. Then Captain Watson had his hands on the man and threw him against the rail.

Alec saw the man's eyes turn to the lifeboat that was being lowered. Before the captain could stop him, he was climbing over the rail. He was going to jump into the boat! Suddenly the *Drake* lurched. The man lost his balance and, screaming, fell into the water. He never rose to the surface.

The dark-skinned man had drowned. Immediately Alec thought of the Black. What was happening to him? Was he still in his stall? Alec fought his way out of line and toward the stern of the boat. If the stallion was alive, he was going to set him free and give him his chance to fight for life.

The stall was still standing. Alec heard a shrill whistle rise above the storm. He rushed to the door, lifted the heavy bar and swung it open. For a second the mighty hoofs stopped pounding and there was silence. Alec backed slowly away.

Then he saw the Black, his head held high, his nostrils blown out with excitement. Suddenly he snorted and plunged straight for the rail and Alec. Alec was paralysed, he couldn't move. One hand was on the rail, which was broken at this point, leaving nothing between him and the open water. The Black swerved as he came near him, and the boy realized that the stallion was making for the hole. The horse's shoulder grazed him as he swerved, and Alec went flying into space. He felt the water close over his head.

When he came up, his first thought was of the ship; then he heard an explosion, and he saw the *Drake* settling deep into the water. Frantically he looked around for a lifeboat, but there was none in sight. Then he saw the Black swimming not more than ten yards away. Something swished by him—a rope, and it was attached to the Black's halter! The same rope that they had used to bring the stallion aboard the boat, and which they had never been able to get close enough to the horse to untie. Without stopping to think, Alec grabbed hold of it. Then he was pulled through the water, into the oncoming seas.

The waves were still large, but with the aid of his life jacket, Alec was able to stay on top. He was too tired now to give much thought to what he had done. He only knew that he had had his choice of remaining in the water alone or being pulled by the Black. If he was to die, he would rather die with the mighty stallion than alone. He took one last look behind and saw the *Drake* sink into the depths.

For hours Alec battled the waves. He had tied the rope securely around his waist. He could hardly hold his head up. Suddenly he felt the rope slacken. The Black had stopped swimming! Alec anxiously waited; peering into the darkness he could just make out the head of the stallion. The Black's whistle pierced the air! After a few minutes, the rope became taut again. The horse had changed his direction. Another hour passed, then the storm diminished to high, rolling swells. The first streaks of dawn appeared on the horizon.

The Black had stopped four times during the night, and each time he had altered his course. Alec wondered whether the stallion's wild instinct was leading him to land. The sun rose and shone down brightly on the boy's head; the salt water he had swallowed during the night made him sick to his stomach. But when Alec felt that he could hold out no longer, he looked at the struggling, fighting animal in front of him, and new courage came to him.

Suddenly he realized that they were going with the waves, instead of against them. He shook his head, trying to clear his mind. Yes, they were riding in; they must be approaching land! Eagerly he strained his salt-filled eyes and looked into the distance. And then he saw it—about a quarter of a mile away was a small island, not much more than sandy reef in the sea. But he might find food and water there, and have a chance to survive. Faster and faster they approached the white sand. They were in the breakers. The Black's scream shattered the stillness. He was able to walk; he staggered a little and shook his black head. Then his action shifted marvellously, and he went faster through the shallow water.

Alec's head whirled as he was pulled toward the beach with ever-increasing speed. Suddenly he realized the danger of his posi-

tion. He must untie this rope from around his waist, or else he would be dragged to death over the sand! Desperately his fingers flew to the knot; it was tight, he had made sure of that. Frantically he worked on it as the shore drew closer and closer.

The Black was now on the beach. Thunder began to roll from beneath his hoofs as he broke out of the water. Hours in the water had swelled the knot—Alec couldn't untie it! Then he remembered his pocketknife. Could it still be there? Alec's hand darted to his rear pants pocket. His fingers reached inside and came out with the knife.

He was now on the beach being dragged by the stallion; the sand flew in his face. Quickly he opened the knife and began to cut the rope. His body burned from the sand, his clothes were being torn off of him! His speed was increasing every second! Madly he sawed away at the rope. With one final thrust he was through! His outflung hands caressed the sand. As he closed his eyes, his parched lips murmured, "Yes—Uncle Ralph—it did—come in handy."

THERE'S A FLY IN MY SOUP!

There's a fly in my soup!
Don't worry, sir, he won't drink much.

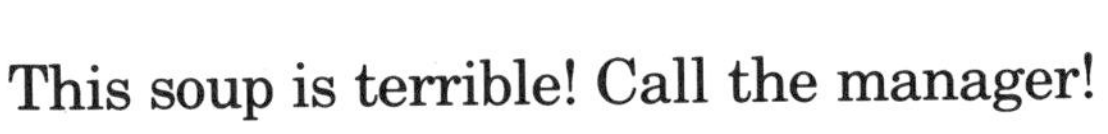

This soup is terrible! Call the manager!
He won't eat it either, sir.

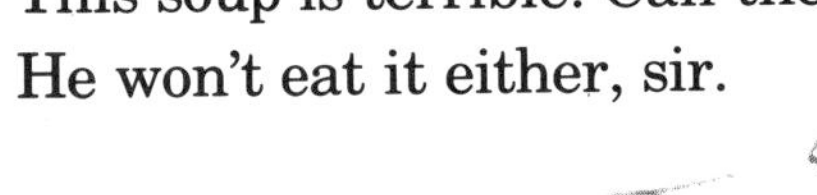

There's a fly in my soup!
Well, keep quiet about it or everyone will want one.

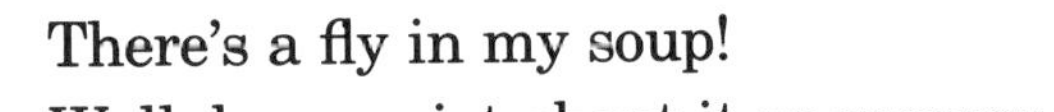

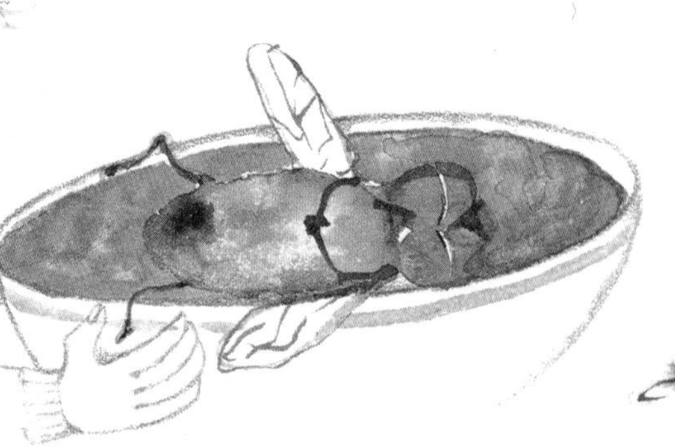

There's a dead fly in my soup!
Yes, sir, it's the hot water that kills 'em.

Do you serve crabs?
Sit down, sir—we serve anybody.

There's a fly in my soup!
The little rascals don't care what they eat, do they?

What's this in my soup?
I dunno, sir, I can't tell one bug from another.

There's a fly in my soup!
Yes, the chef used to be a tailor.

I asked for bread with my dinner.
It's in the sausages, sir.

There's a dead beetle in my soup.
Yes sir, they're not very good swimmers.

There's a spider in my soup!
Oh, really? That's 10¢ extra.

Acknowledgements
Jack and Old Strongman: From AMERICAN FOLK TALES & SONGS by Richard Chase. Reprinted by permission of Dover Publications, Inc. *The Boy Who Turned Into a TV Set:* Excerpt from THE BOY WHO TURNED INTO A TV SET by Stephen Manes. Reprinted by permission of Coward, McCann & Geoghehan, text copyright © 1979 by Stephen Manes. *Me and the Weirdos:* From ME AND THE WEIRDOS by Jane Sutton. Copyright © 1981 by Jane Sutton. Reprinted by permission of Houghton Mifflin Company. *Dear Mr. Henshaw:* Letters to Mr. Henshaw (pp. 1-8) from DEAR MR. HENSHAW by Beverly Cleary. Copyright © 1983 by Beverly Cleary. By permission of William Morrow & Company, Inc. *Last One into Bed* and *The Itch:* From QUICK LET'S GET OUT OF HERE by Michael Rosen. Copyright © 1983 by Michael Rosen. Reprinted by permission of André Deutsch Ltd. *The Doughnuts:* From HOMER PRICE by Robert McCloskey. Copyright 1943 by Robert McCloskey, renewed © 1971 by Robert McCloskey. Reprinted by permission of Viking Penguin, Inc. *Company Manners:* From JAMBOREE RHYMES FOR ALL TIMES by Eve Merriam. Copyright © 1962, 1964, 1966, 1973, 1984 by Eve Merriam. All Rights Reserved. Reprinted by permission of Marian Reiner for the Author. *How to Eat a Poem:* From IT DOESN'T ALWAYS HAVE TO RHYME by Eve Merriam. Copyright © 1964 by Eve Merriam. All Rights Reserved. Reprinted by permission of Marian Reiner for the Author. *Sneaky Bill, Banananananananana, Good News, Just for a Change, Back Yard, July Night,* and *Can't Deny It:* By William Cole. Copyright © William Cole 1962, 1969, 1972, 1975, 1977. Reprinted from A BOY NAMED MARY JANE AND OTHER SILLY VERSE by William Cole. Reprinted with permission. *Listen to the Hodja:* Reprinted by permission from PLAYS FROM FOLK-TALES OF AFRICA AND ASIA, by Barbara Winther. Copyright © 1976 by Barbara Winther, Publishers Plays, Inc., Boston MA USA. *Tales of the Hodja:* © Charles Downing 1964. Reprinted from TALES OF THE HODJA retold by Charles Downing (1964) by permission of Oxford University Press and David McKay Company, Inc.

Harriet the Spy: From Chapter 1 (pp. 8-20) in HARRIET THE SPY by Louise Fitzhugh. Copyright © 1964 by Louise Fitzhugh. Reprinted by permission of Harper & Row, Publishers, Inc. *Silver* and *The Horseman:* Reprinted by permission of The Literary Trustees of Walter de la Mare and The Society of Authors as their representative. *My Shoes* and *I Wonder:* By Siv Cedering Fox from THE BLUE HORSE AND OTHER NIGHT POEMS by Siv Cedering Fox. Copyright © 1976, 1977, 1978, 1979 by Siv Cedering Fox. Reprinted by permisson of Clarion Books/Ticknor & Fields, a Houghton Mifflin Company. *Face to Face:* by Larry Swartz. *Autumn Song of the Goose:* From RING OF EARTH, copyright © 1986 by Jane Yolen. Reprinted by permission of Harcourt Brace Jovanovich, Inc. *Sasquatch* and *Water Monsters:* From A NEW WORLD BESTIARY written by Mary Hamilton and illustrated by Kim LaFave. © Douglas and McIntyre 1985. *Tiger Watch:* Copyright © 1982 by Jan Wahl. Reprinted by permission of Harcourt Brace Jovanovich, Inc. *Ruins:* By Harry Behn from CRICKETS AND BULLFROGS AND WHISPERS OF THUNDER: Poems & Pictures by Harry Behn. Copyright 1949, 1953, © 1956, 1957, 1966, 1968 by Harry Behn. Copyright renewed 1977 by Alice L. Behn, Copyright renewed 1981 by Alice Behn Goebel, Pamela Behn Adam, Prescott Behn, and Peter Behn. Reprinted by permission of Marian Reiner.

The Frost Giants: Excerpt from d'Aulaires' TROLLS by Edgar and Ingri Parin d'Aulaire. Copyright © 1972 by Ingri and Edgar Parin d'Aulaire. Reprinted by permission of Doubleday & Company, Inc. *Beauty and the Beast:* From CANADIAN FAIRY TALES, retold by Eva Martin, Groundwood Books/Douglas & McIntyre, 1984 and from TALES OF THE FAR NORTH by Eva Martin. Text copyright © 1984 by Eva Martin, Reprinted by permission of the publisher, Dial Books for Young Readers. *The Crystal Child:* Chapter 1 (pp. 1-10) from THE CRYSTAL CHILD by Barbara Wersba. Text copyright © 1982 by Barbara Wersba. Reprinted by permission of Harper & Row, Publishers, Inc. *The Phantom Tollboth:* From THE PHANTOM TOLLBOOTH, by Norton Juster. Copyright © 1961 by Norton Juster. Reprinted by permission of Random House, Inc. *The Lion, the Witch and the Wardrobe:* Extract from THE LION, THE WITCH AND THE WARDROBE, © C.S. Lewis 1950, published by William Collins & Sons Ltd. *Pushed* and *Lost His Marbles:* by Diane Dawber. By permission of Borealis Press Ltd, from OATMEAL MITTENS, © 1987. *Ned Kelly and the City of the Bees:* Chapter 5, "Ned Kelly Meets the Queen," from NED KELLY AND THE CITY OF THE BEES by Thomas Keneally. Copyright © 1978 by Thomas Keneally. Reprinted by permission of the publishers, Jonathan Cape Ltd. and David R. Godine, Publisher, Inc. *The Stars in the Sky:* From THE MAID OF THE NORTH retold by Ethel Johnston Phelps. Copyright © 1981 by Ethel Johnston Phelps. Reprinted by permission of Henry Holt and Company. *The Long-Haired Boy:* From WHERE THE SIDEWALK ENDS: The Poems & Drawings of Shel Silverstein. Copyright © 1974 by Snake Eye Music, Inc. Reprinted by permission of Harper & Row, Publishers, Inc.

The Happy Orpheline: Excerpt from Chapter 6 (pp. 82-84) in THE HAPPY ORPHELINE by Natalie Savage Carlson. Text Copyright © 1957 by Natalie Savage Carlson. Reprinted by permission of Harper & Row, Publishers, Inc. *Nothing's Fair in Fifth Grade:* From NOTHING'S FAIR IN FIFTH GRADE, by Barthe De Clements. Copyright © 1981 by Barthe De Clements. Reprinted by permission of Viking Penguin, Inc. *Getting To Know You:* Copyright © 1951 by Richard Rodgers and Oscar Hammerstein II. Copyright renewed; Williamson Music Co., owner of publication and allied rights throughout the Western Hemisphere and Japan. International Copyright Secured. All rights reserved. Used by permission of Chappel Music Canada Limited. *Hockeybat Harris:* Copyright © 1984 by Geoffrey Bilson, Published by Kids Can Press, Toronto. *Bridge to Terabithia:* Abridged from pages 38-43, 44-47 in BRIDGE TO TERABITHIA by Katherine Paterson (Thomas Y. Crowell). Copyright © 1977 by Katherine Paterson. By permission of Harper & Row, Publishers, Inc. *Today We Are Brother and Sister:* "Brother," "Sister," "Together," and "We race down the beach" from TODAY WE ARE BROTHER AND SISTER by Arnold Adoff. Copyright © 1981 by Arnold Adoff. By permission of Lothrop, Lee & Shepard Books (A Division of William Morrow & Company). *A Taste of Blackberries:* Chapter 4 (pp. 25-31) from A TASTE OF BLACKBERRIES by Doris Buchanan Smith (Thomas Y. Crowell). Copyright © 1973 by Doris Buchanan Smith. Reprinted by permission of Harper & Row, Publishers, Inc. *The Twelve Days of Christmas North:* By Lois Barber from THE TWELVE DAYS OF CHRISTMAS NORTH. Reprinted with permission of Northern Times Press. *Honor Bound:* Chapter 11 "Visitors" from HONOR BOUND by Mary Alice and John Downie © Oxford University Press Canada 1971. Reprinted by permission. *From Anna:* Abridged from pages 140-145, 155-164 in FROM ANNA by Jean Little. Text Copyright © 1972 by Jean Little. Reprinted by permission of Harper & Row, Publishers, Inc. *Going Through the Old Photos:* From QUICK LET'S GET OUT OF HERE by Michael Rosen. Copyright © 1983 by Michael Rosen. Reprinted by permission of André Deutsch Ltd.

Golden Mare: By William C. McGraw. *Emily Carr:* By Grant Heckman. *The Truce of the Forest Fire:* By Ted Ashlee. Reprinted by permission of Ted Ashlee. *Wild Mouse:* By Irene Brady. Reprinted by permission of Irene Brady. *Orange Kitten, Charm for a Sick Dog, But I See Sparrows!* and *I Sing to the Stars:* by Nancy Prasad. Reprinted by permission of the author. *The Midnight Fox:* By Betsy Byars. Copyright © 1968 by Betsy Byars. Reprinted by permission of Viking Penguin Inc. *A Place for Margaret:* By Bernice Thurman Hunter. Copyright 1984. Reprinted by permission of Scholastic-TAB Publications Ltd. *Anywhere:* by Prince Redcloud. Used by permission of the author and his representative, Lee Bennett Hopkins. *Diary of an R.C.M.P. Horse Trainer:* Reprinted from OWL Magazine with permission of the publisher, the Young Naturalist Foundation. *The Ghost Horse of the Mounties:* By sean o huigin. Reprinted by permission of Black Moss Press. *The Black Stallion:* Condensed from THE BLACK STALLION, "Homeward Bound" and "The Storm" pages 3-21, by Walter Farley. Copyright 1941 and renewed 1969 by Walter Farley. Reprinted by permission of Random House, Inc.

Care has been taken to trace the ownership of copyright material used in this text. The publishers welcome any information enabling them to correct any reference or credit in subsequent editions.